Frontispiece

Stool with helical stem illustrating the bending properties of elm

SOLID AND LAMINATED WOOD BENDING

BY

W. C. STEVENS, M.A., A.M.I.Mech.E.,
AND
N. TURNER

Forest Products Research Laboratory

Fredonia Books
Amsterdam, The Netherlands

Solid and Laminated Wood Bending

by
W. C. Stevens
N. Turner

for Forest Products Research Laboratory

ISBN: 1-4101-0901-1

Reprinted from the 1952 edition

Fredonia Books
Amsterdam, The Netherlands
http://www.fredoniabooks.com

PREFATORY NOTE

THE purpose of this book is to meet the demand for information on the processes of wood bending, as reflected in the many enquiries addressed to this Laboratory. It is largely a handbook of practice, and is thus written from the practical viewpoint, with such theoretical background as suffices to explain the adoption of the various procedures It would not be possible, and indeed the authors have not attempted, to deal with the many special variants of bending processes in commercial use. All of these rest upon the nature of the timber to be bent and upon the application of certain general principles, which are here set forth and clarified by the detailed treatment of such typical examples as will serve to give a lead to the ingenuity of the individual user for his own needs.

Thanks are due to members of the trade for permission to use photographs illustrating some of the processes, and each is acknowledged in the appropriate place.

F. Y. HENDERSON
Director

FOREST PRODUCTS RESEARCH LABORATORY,
Princes Risborough,
Aylesbury,
Bucks.

July, 1948.

iii

CONTENTS

PART II

LAMINATED BENDING

LIST OF ILLUSTRATIONS

PLATES

FIGURES

SOLID AND LAMINATED WOOD BENDING

INTRODUCTION

THE practice of bending timber dates back to antiquity when man first learnt to make baskets from osier and shipwrights no longer contented themselves with making boats from hollowed-out logs. Since wood in its natural state has strongly marked elastic properties which render it resilient, a bend made from such material would retain its shape only so long as it was securely held in place by adjacent members of a structure. Moreover, it would be extremely difficult, if not quite impossible, to bend thick pieces to a small radius of curvature, and curved boat stems, for example, would undoubtedly be hewn or sawn from limbs of trees having a curvature roughly the same as that required. This method of producing curved members, though still practised in the boat-building industry of to-day, has very obvious limitations, and in the production of various curved parts and members commonly required for the manufacture of vehicles, furniture, etc., the timber is usually obtained in board or scantling form and either bandsawn or bent to shape. If the thickness of the portion to be bent is small as compared with the radius of curvature, and if this portion is firmly to be held in position by adjacent structural parts when bent, wood in its natural or in its dried state may be employed. There is, of course, theoretically no limit to the radius of curvature or thickness of curved parts produced by bandsawing, but this method has two distinct disadvantages. In the first place, when band-sawing a curved piece of comparatively small radius of curvature it becomes necessary to saw some portion of it across the grain of the wood, with consequent appreciable reduction in the strength of the piece as a whole. Secondly, the awkwardly shaped portions that are cut away often constitute a very serious conversion loss. Fortunately, there are means by which straight pieces of timber may be bent to shape and caused to retain this shape without necessarily receiving support from adjacent structural members. There are two main methods of doing this : one by softening and bending the complete piece in the solid, and the other by bending and gluing together a number of thin laminæ sufficient to produce finally a built-up piece of the required dimension and curvature. Considerable experience with both methods has been gained at the Forest Products Research Laboratory, and although it cannot be claimed that all possible forms of bending technique have been fully investigated, a considerable body of information is now available from which to draw. In commercial practice several factors need to be considered when deciding the method to be adopted, such as production costs, facilities available, quality and species of timber to be used, etc. It is proposed in what follows to describe in some detail various methods commonly employed for bending wood in solid and laminated form and to give some idea of the scope and limitations of each.

Most, though not all, of the methods to be described have been tested at the Laboratory, and although it is hoped that the descriptions may prove useful to such as are engaged in, or contemplate undertaking, work of this nature, it needs to be stressed that success in bending depends as much upon the skill and experience of the operators as upon any theoretical or technical knowledge to be acquired from books.

The Principles of Wood Bending

In the bending of wood or other elastic materials it is usual to assume that transverse plane sections remain plane and normal to the longitudinal fibres, which is to say that end sections initially square with the faces of a piece remain square during the process of bending. From this it follows that, in the bent state, the lengths of the convex and concave faces are no longer equal, as they were when originally cut. The difference in these lengths is produced in consequence of induced compressive stresses causing fibres on the concave face to shorten, and induced tensile stresses causing fibres on the convex face to stretch.

Wood in its natural state exhibits elastic properties over a limited stress range, which implies that strain is proportional to stress and that when imposed stresses are removed the strains likewise disappear and the wood returns to its original state and dimensions. It follows, in consequence, that if the limiting stress is not exceeded anywhere in the piece, a bend made from such material will spring back to its original shape when the forces causing it to bend are removed. When, however, this limiting stress value is exceeded, proportionality between stress and strain no longer exists and, on removal of the stress, some permanent deformation is usually observed to have taken place. Further stressing will ultimately induce strains sufficient to cause fracturing of the piece, and these fractures generally become apparent first in the stretched convex face. Maximum strain intensities will naturally occur on the extreme inner and outer surfaces of a bent piece and will increase as the radius of bend decreases for any given thickness. The limiting radius is thus dependent upon the magnitude of the strains that can be induced on these faces without at the same time causing fractures.

Most common timbers in their natural state cannot be bent to an appreciably small radius of curvature without either fracturing, or retaining elastic properties sufficient to cause them to spring back to approximately their original shape on removal of the bending forces. Many timbers, however, when subjected to heat treatments in the presence of moisture such, for instance, as steaming or boiling, become semi-plastic, in that their compressibility is very considerably increased and comparatively small compressive stresses are capable of producing very appreciable strains without fracturing the material. Such treatments have much less effect upon the tensile properties of these woods, and the limiting radius of curvature now becomes dependent mainly on the maximum permissible tensile stress and the strain of the stretched fibres near the convex face. Even so, this limiting radius may be much smaller than before, since appreciably more shortening of the fibres near the concave face may occur before the breaking point in tension is reached than when no treatment is applied. In a bend made from untreated wood, the " neutral axis ", along which no change in length has occurred, coincides much more closely with a line situated midway between the convex and concave surfaces than a bend made from treated material. In the latter, there is a pronounced tendency for the " neutral axis " to move towards the convex surface, so that appreciably more of the wood may be in compression than in tension (see Fig. 1).

A second factor of considerable importance, introduced as a result of the heat treatment, is the tendency of the now more plastic material to retain its shape after bending, particularly if dried under restraint. By holding such material to shape after bending then cooling and drying it to a low moisture content, the wood tends eventually to become rigid and " set " almost exactly to the curved shape imposed on it by bending.

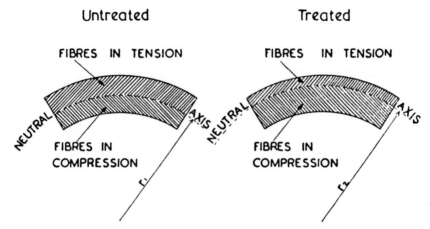

Fig. 1—*Effect of steaming treatment on the position of the neutral axis in a bend*

The precise mechanism involved in the plastic deformation of stressed heat-treated wood is not fully understood, nor can it be stated with certainty why some woods are considerably more susceptible to such treatment than others. In general, most of the home-grown hardwoods react favourably to treatment, but many of the exotic hardwoods and most of the softwoods are refractory in this respect and hence are little suited to bending in solid form. The manner in which a good bending species, such as beech, will react is illustrated in Figs. 2 and 3, which show the stress/strain relationships in tension and compression of sample specimens before and after steaming. These show clearly that the effect of the treatment is :

(*a*) to cause the compressive strain to increase rapidly with stress above a certain value ;

(*b*) to increase very considerably the ultimate strain in compression ; but

(*c*) to induce only comparatively slight changes in the tensile properties of the wood.

It has already been shown that the maximum stress and strain in tension determine the limiting radius of curvature for fractureless bending and, in practice, it will be found that the stretched convex face will tend to fracture long before the compressed concave face has been strained to the limit. Obviously, were it possible to impose the maximum permissible compression on the concave face of a bend without at the same time inducing such stress on the fibres near the convex face as to strain them beyond the limit, the radius of curvature could be decreased yet further. This, in effect, is the

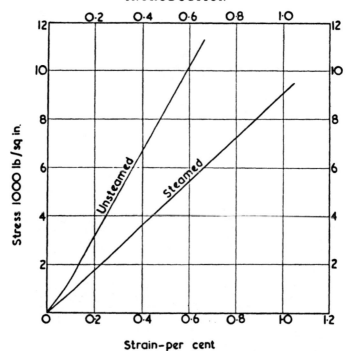

Strain-per cent

FIG.2—*Effect of steaming on the stress/strain relationship in tension of home-grown beech*

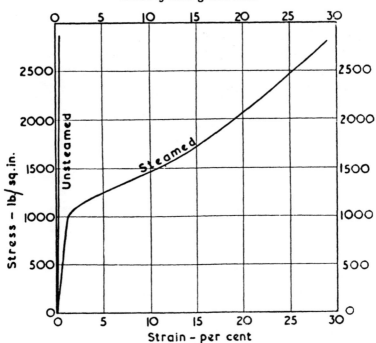

Strain - per cent

FIG. 3—*Effect of steaming on the stress/strain relationship in compression of home grown beech*

underlying principle of the method of bending with the aid of a supporting strap.

In the normal application of this method the stretched convex face is supported by means of a band of steel, or other suitable material, placed over and secured to it in such a way that the strain is limited by mechanical restraint. In its simplest form this band or strap consists of a thin steel strip to which are fitted wooden or steel angles, or end-stops, that bear closely on the ends of the piece to be bent. Neglecting the stretch in the steel, and assuming the end-stops fit closely initially, it follows that during the bending process, virtually no stretching of the fibres can take place and that the limiting radius is dependent now solely upon the ultimate strain in compression.

In actual practice a certain amount of stretch is permitted, and in certain instances special adjustable end-stops are fitted so as to regulate the amount, but in no case should this be allowed to exceed the breaking point if fractures are to be avoided. A typical failure in tension resulting from the lack of adequate support is shown in Plate 2, and a typical failure occasioned by over-compressing the inner face of a bend is illustrated in Plate 3. The smallest possible radius of curvature for any piece of wood is attained when both the inner and outer surfaces are on the point of fracturing.

Part I

SOLID BENDING

CHAPTER I

THE SELECTION AND PREPARATION OF BENDING MATERIAL

Quality

IN selecting wood for bending it must be borne in mind that appreciable compressive strains are likely to be imposed upon the fibres and the structure generally, so that if planes of weakness exist, caused by the presence of defects such as knots, ingrown bark, surface checks, etc., fractures will start and develop in and around these planes when comparatively little straining has occurred. In order to minimize losses occasioned by failure of the wood in bending, therefore, the use of timber containing such defects should be avoided as far as possible. Should it prove impossible to eliminate such defects entirely, the bending blank should be set up so that the defect is near the convex face and hence near or on the neutral axis, where no strains are imposed. Ideally, straight-grained, clear material should be specially selected for bending work, particularly if the bend to be made is severe in character.

Species

In selecting a species of timber suitable for the job in hand, several factors need to be taken into consideration, such as availability of material, bending properties, strength properties of the material after bending, etc. Bent furniture parts, for instance, are usually made of beech or oak, since these timbers are in reasonable supply, have good bending properties and are much used for the manufacture of furniture in general. The manufacturer of sports goods, however, would select such species as ash or hickory for the production of hockey and lacrosse sticks, as much on account of the resilience of such timbers as by virtue of their bending properties. Some idea of the bending properties of a number of timbers may be obtained from an examination of the list given in Table I. This table has been compiled from data obtained at the Forest Products Research Laboratory with the object of indicating the safe radius of curvature to which certain timbers may be bent, so that only about 5 per cent of the total number of bent pieces will fracture during the process. It needs to be added that the data in the table refer to good quality, air-dried material, 1 inch thick and steamed at atmospheric pressure.

The influence that supporting straps have on the limiting radius of curvature is indicated very clearly in this table, and the greatly superior bending qualities of such woods as elm, ash and beech as compared with, say, mahogany, teak and spruce, also become very apparent. It may be of interest to note that there is not a great difference in the bending properties of ash, beech and oak despite the fact that the first-named is commonly regarded as being a bending timber " par excellence ".

6

TABLE I*.—*Approximate Radius of Curvature (in Inches) at Which Breakages during Bending should not exceed 5 Per Cent.*

Species	When supporting straps	
	are used	are not used
" African walnut " (*Lovoa klaineana*)	12.0	—
Ash, American (*Fraxinus* sp.) (imported)	4.5	13.0
Ash, European (*Fraxinus excelsior*) (home-grown)	2.5	12.0
Ayan (*Distemonanthus benthamianus*)	20.0	32.0
Banak (*Virola merendonis*)	30.0	48.0
Beech, European (*Fagus sylvatica*) (imported)	4.0	14.5
Beech, European (home-grown)	1.5	13.0
Beech, Southland (*Nothofagus menziesii*)	10.0	20.0
Birch, Canadian yellow (*Betula ?lutea*) (imported)	3.0	17.0
Blackbutt (*Eucalyptus pilularis*)	24.0	48.0
Cabbage-bark, Black (*Lonchocarpus castilloi*)	30.0	—
Camphorwood, East African (*Ocotea usambarensis*)	14.0	27.0
Crabwood (*Carapa guianensis*)	30.0	48.0
Cramantee (*Guarea excelsa*)	18.0	32.0
Danta (*Cistanthera papaverifera*)	14.0	30.0
Elm, Dutch (*Ulmus hollandica* var. *major*) (home-grown)	Less than 0.5	9.5
Eng (*Dipterocarpus tuberculatus*)	10.0	32.0
Greenheart (*Ocotea rodiaei*)	12.0	56.0
Guarea (*Guarea thompsonii*)	14.0	36.0
Guarea (*Guarea cedrata*)	7.5	20.0
Gurjun (*Dipterocarpus* sp.) (Ceylon)	30.0	—
Gurjun (*Dipterocarpus* sp.) (Indian)	30.0	—
Horse-chestnut, European (*Aesculus hippocastanum*) (home-grown)	4.0	8.0
Idigbo (*Terminalia ivorensis*)	32.0	44.0
Iroko (*Chlorophora excelsa*)	16.0	—
Karri (*Eucalyptus diversicolor*) (South African)	8.0	12.5
Keruing (*Dipterocarpus* sp.)	30.0	60.0
Mahogany, African (*Khaya ivorensis*)	37.0	31.0
Mahogany, African (Uganda) (*Khaya anthotheca*)	18.0	20.0
Mahogany, Central American (*Swietenia macrophylla*)	12.0	28.0
Mora (*Mora excelsa*)	13.0	32.0
Mufumbi (*Entandrophragma utile*)	20.0	56.0
Mujua (*Alstonia congensis*)	31.0	—
Mukusu (*Entandrophragma angolense*)	24.0	40.0
Musisi (*Maesopsis eminii*)	40.0	60.0
Nargusta (*Terminalia amazonia*)	30.0	—
Oak, American white (*Quercus* sp.)	0.5	13.0
Oak, European (*Quercus robur*) (home-grown)	2.0	13.0
Oak, Japanese (*Quercus* sp.)	1.5	12.0
Obeche (*Triplochiton scleroxylon*)	12.0	28.0
Odoko (*Scottellia coriacea*)	30.0	60.0
Olive, E. African (*Olea hochstetteri*)	13.0	30.0
Opepe (*Sarcocephalus diderrichii*)	30.0	—
Pine, British Honduras pitch (*Pinus caribaea*)	14.0	28.0
Podo (*Podocarpus* sp.)	18.0	20.0
" Queensland walnut " (*Endiandra palmerstonii*)	20.0	44.0
Robinia (*Robinia pseudoacacia*) (home-grown)	1.5	11.0
Santa maria (or jacareuba) (*Calophyllum braziliense*)	20.0	56.0
Spruce, European (*Picea abies*) (imported)	30.0	—
" Tasmanian oak " (*Eucalyptus obliqua*)	16.0	24.0
,, ,, (*Eucalyptus regnans*)	30.0	30.0
Teak (*Tectona grandis*)	16.0	28.0
Timbersweet (*Nectandra* or *Ocotea* sp.)	20.0	—
Waika chewstick (*Symphonia globulifera*)	28.0	—
Yellowwood, British Honduras (*Podocarpus guatemalensis*)	35.0	36.0
Yemeri (*Vochysia hondurensis*)	30.0	40.0

Chestnut, Sweet (*Castanea sativa*) ; Hickory (*Carya* sp.) ; Hornbeam (*Carpinus betulus*); Oak, Turkey (home-grown) (*Quercus cerris*) ; Plane, London (*Platanus acerifolia*) ; Walnut (*Juglans nigra* and *regia*) ; Yew (*Taxus baccata*).	Good bending properties but no exact data available.

*See Supplement to Table I (p. 68).

Ash, though undoubtedly an excellent bending wood, is unusually susceptible to the presence of pin knots near the compression face, which are very prone to produce buckling or compression failures. Moreover, if the grain runs out on the tension face, there is a pronounced tendency for it to "lift" when the strap is finally removed. Elm, on the other hand, has exceptionally good bending qualities and appears generally to be remarkably tolerant of defects, though naturally, as in all woods, they have an adverse effect upon the bending properties.

Trees

Having once decided upon the species and quality of the timber required for a particular job, the question next arises as to what precautions should be taken to ensure that the trees selected to yield the timber shall, in fact, provide the maximum quantity of material most suitable for the purpose. On this subject there are considerable differences of opinion, and few bending firms seem entirely to be in agreement as to the distinguishing features that mark good quality bending timber in the round. Factors such as age, rate of growth, soil characteristics, etc., undoubtedly have a bearing on the subject, though from tests carried out at the Laboratory the indications are that, provided clear, straight-grown material can be obtained, such factors are of secondary importance.

There are indications, however, that the best bending ash, for instance, is to be obtained on well drained soil, particularly in the red sandstone districts. For most timbers, also, the second length above the spread of the butt provides the best material, and portions taken from near the heart are generally to be avoided. Very old trees, or trees that have grown either very rapidly or very slowly, do not usually yield the best material, which for ash should have about 10 rings to the inch.

Trees attacked by fungus of any sort are worthless for bending, as the wood is liable to be brittle and pieces cut from them become prone to break right across the section during the bending operation.

Moisture Content

With regard to the seasoning of the timber, most can be bent in the green state soon after felling, though some bending firms advocate leaving the timber in log form for a period before conversion. Some woods, such as wych elm, sweet chestnut and oak, if bent while green to small radii of curvature, are liable to rupture as a result of hydraulic pressures induced within the moisture-laden cells (see Plate 5). Apart from the fact that the forces required for bending are rather greater, it may be said that the properties of wood air-dried to, say, 25 per cent moisture content differ little from similar material in the green state. Experience has shown, moreover, that supporting straps can be removed with impunity sooner after bending air-dried than green material and that a shorter time is required for drying and setting to shape, with reduced tendency for the bend to distort or split during this process.

The disadvantages of using air-dried material are (1) that fine surface checks which may have developed in seasoning and have passed unnoticed may result in compression failures, (2) that the steaming treatment in wetting the dried wood may cause it to distort before bending, and (3) that bending by hand is rendered more arduous.

The effect of drying-checks on the bending properties are shown in Plate 6.

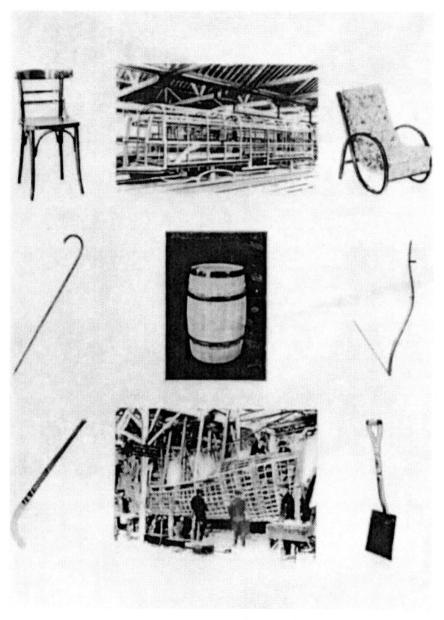

Dining chair—Courtesy of William Birch & Sons, Ltd.
Arm chair — ,,   ,, Risborough Furniture, Ltd.
Tram body — ,,   ,, Brush Coachwork, Ltd.
Spade   — ,,   ,. Isaac Nash & Sons, Ltd.
Lifeboat   — ,,   ,. Royal National Life-Boat Institution.

PLATE 1—Examples of solid bends as used in industry

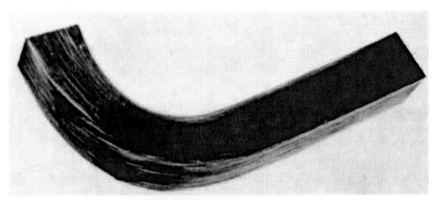

PLATE 2—Typical failure resulting from lack of adequate support on the convex face of a bend

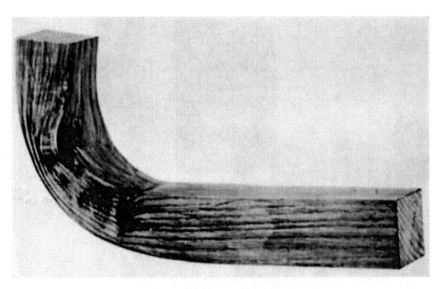

PLATE 3—Typical failure resulting from over-compressing the concave face of a bend

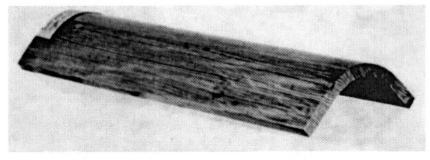

PLATE 4—Scots pine board bent across the grain

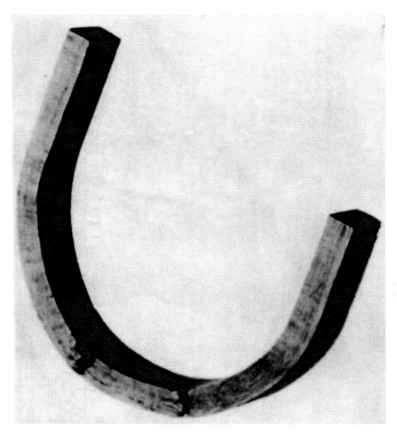

PLATE 5—Typical failure occasioned by bending thick oak in the green state

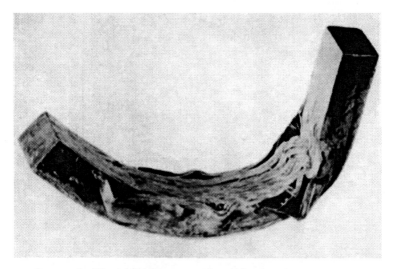

PLATE 6—Typical failure occasioned by bending material containing surface checks

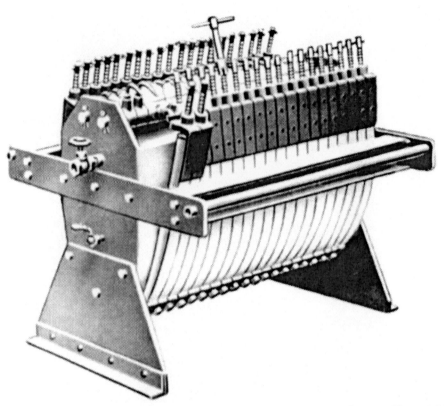

PLATE 7—Steam-heated metal form

PLATE 8—Austrian chair back type of bend

Machining

Once a decision has been reached regarding the species, quality and selection of the timber, it remains to prepare the blanks or specimens for the softening treatment. These should all be cut exactly to length with squared ends, leaving sufficient material for nailing tie-bars in the manner later to be described, if this operation is found to be necessary. Allowances must be made for some distortion of the cross-section during bending, for subsequent shrinkage and for the inevitable deviations from the exact shape required, which are to be associated with solid bending. A smooth surface on the blanks is very desirable since ridges tend to induce unnecessary buckling, and, for this reason, planed and smooth-finished material is to be preferred to material straight from the saw. It is quite possible to bend shaped or moulded material of round section, but where this is undertaken it must be remembered that the bending process always tends to flatten the surfaces in contact with the form and strap, bringing these closer together and at the same time causing lateral expansion of the piece. Frequently such sectional distortion is of no consequence, or can be made so by subsequent sanding of the bent part.

Experience has shown that slash-sawn material, cut and bent so that the annual rings are roughly parallel to the face of the form, gives results slightly better than quarter-sawn material bent with the rings normal to the face of the form, but the trouble entailed in securing this result would hardly be justified except, possibly, in the case of very severe types of bend.

CHAPTER II

SOFTENING TREATMENTS

Steaming

IN order to render certain woods plastic and compressible so that they are in the best possible condition for bending, a supply of heat and moisture must be made available.

It has already been shown that wood at 25-30 per cent moisture content contains as much moisture as is necessary to render it compressible when heated. Numerous tests made at the Laboratory have failed to show that any marked improvement in the bending qualities of wood can be obtained by heating it to a temperature much above the boiling point of water, i.e. 212° F. (100° C.). Probably the commonest and most suitable method of obtaining the required conditions is to subject the timber to saturated steam at atmospheric pressure in a steam chest such as the one illustrated in Fig. 4.

The essentials of such a steaming chamber are that sufficient steam is made available to maintain a temperature of 100° C. and that means are provided for readily introducing and removing the wood to be bent.

Racks or shelves for holding the timber need to be provided, and it must be remembered that such a wood as oak, if placed in contact with iron or steel, is liable to become badly stained. In order to economize in steam the chest should be lagged and, provided the desired temperature can be maintained, exhaust steam from an engine may be used and is often preferred. There would appear to be no great advantage in using steam at a pressure higher than that of the atmosphere, as the bending properties of wood are not markedly increased at the higher pressures. The disadvantages of using high pressure steam are that the chest must be made strong enough to withstand the internal pressure, and that before the door can be opened care must be taken to ensure

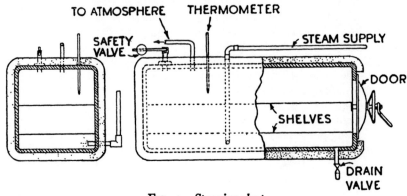

FIG. 4—*Steaming chest*

that the pressure has dropped to zero, thus entailing a loss in production time.

Very high pressures have been found to be very detrimental to certain timbers and to result in serious discoloration.

Wood is in the best possible condition for bending when it has been heated right through to the boiling point temperature, and, as a rough guide, $\frac{3}{4}$ hour per inch of thickness should suffice to effect this. No improvement in the bending properties results from prolonged steaming. The steaming process produces some, but not extensive, drying of green timber, but the average moisture content of air-dried wood at, say, 25 per cent moisture content is scarcely altered as a result of the steaming treatment. Very dry wood undoubtedly would pick up a certain amount of moisture, mainly on the surface, but for the most part the effect of steaming is to heat the wood and not to inject steam into the material, as is sometimes supposed.

Other Heating Methods

Wood may be rendered equally suitable for bending by immersing it in boiling water or in heated wet sand. This latter method is often employed in the manufacture of walking sticks and, indeed, it may be said that any treatment that succeeds in heating the timber to about the boiling point, without at the same time causing it to dry very appreciably, will serve to render it fit for bending. As a final illustration of this point, it may be mentioned that rattan canes used for chair-making are usually bent simply by heating the appropriate portions in a naked gas flame and immediately shaping them to the curvature required, without the application of moisture.

Chemical Treatments

Several attempts have been made to render wood suitable for bending by chemical treatments but, to date, no satisfactory method has been discovered. One of the methods suggested consisted of impregnating wood with a saturated solution of urea and then heating the material in an oven at a temperature of 100° C. When thoroughly heated, wood so treated, it was claimed, could be bent to shape either with or without support and would become "set" on cooling. Tests carried out at Forest Products Research Laboratory showed that the bending properties of wood so treated were no different from those of wood that had been steamed or boiled. Furthermore, though it was found that drying, as well as cooling, was not essential for setting bends made of the urea-treated material, exposure of the "set" pieces to high humidity conditions led to very rapid moisture absorption, often sufficient to cause the bends to straighten out completely. Though some improvement has been achieved in this respect, there would still appear to be no material advantage of this process over the more orthodox methods of steaming or boiling.

One other method that has been suggested is to soak wood in tannin solutions which, so it was claimed, would render the wood so pliable that it could be bent in the cold state. Tests carried out at the Laboratory again failed to show that such treatments effected any marked improvement in the bending properties of wood other than might be expected from prolonged soaking of dry wood in cold water.

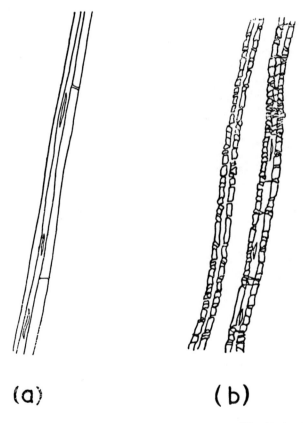

(a)   (b)

(*Magnification about 200*)

Portion of a fibre taken from an untreated control sample, showing the normal condition of the fibre walls.

Portions of two similar fibres taken from the compression side of a bend, showing slip-planes (compression failures) in the fibre walls after maceration.

Fig. 5—*Microscopical examination of beech fibres before and after bending*

Compressed Wood

Precisely how heat treatments render woods compressible to a degree sufficient for bent work is not known, neither is it known why only certain species of timber are appreciably affected in this manner. Microscopical examination of fibres taken from the compressed face of a bend, however, shows that the walls have buckled so as somewhat to resemble a half-closed concertina. Numerous slip planes or incipient compression failures are observable, yet no definite rupture or disintegration of the material as a whole has necessarily occurred. Fig. 5 depicts beech fibres as seen under the microscope before and after steaming and bending, and the slip planes referred to are clearly visible. It needs to be pointed out, however, that in preparing sections for microscopic examination it is necessary to moisten the wood, which as a result tends to resume its initial dimensions, so that the full extent of the buckling induced in bending is not made apparent by such means.

Steamed compressed wood taken from the concave face of a bend has properties differing considerably from those of the untreated material.

In the first place, such wood shows considerable shrinkage and expansion in the longitudinal direction consequent upon limited drying or re-wetting but, at high moisture content values, expansion tends to exceed shrinkage for a given moisture change, which is to say that the wood tends to creep and to resume finally its initial dimensions prior to bending. This tendency explains why solid bends when very wet open out and remain open even when later they are re-dried. Heavily compressed wood, moreover, tends to become pliant and flexible and, in thin sections, may be bent and twisted quite readily between the fingers when cold. Danish and other patents have been taken out for manufacturing " flexible wood " by heat and pressure treatments, but in practice the application of such methods of softening wood are limited by mechanical and economical considerations.

CHAPTER III

HAND BENDING

THE term "hand bending" implies usually that the bending operation is performed manually even though some simple power-multiplying device, such as a lever, is employed to force the pieces to shape. Power-driven bending machinery has certain obvious advantages over hand-operated equipment, but has also certain obvious disadvantages and limitations. The initial cost of installing power-operated machines often proves a factor limiting their use, especially in firms operating in a comparatively small way, or even in larger firms whose output of bent parts is not very great. Furthermore, there are few universal bending machines capable of producing a really large variety of designs, and, indeed, most complicated bends are still almost invariably made by skilled hand-bending operators. Although the requisite skill can only be obtained by experience, suitable and efficient bending equipment is a great asset in such work. The principles of bending, as already outlined, must in all cases be observed if success is to be obtained, but the actual methods and equipment may vary considerably. A description of all possible bending methods and types of bend would fill several volumes, and it is proposed here to outline only some of the methods in general use, and to illustrate apparatus and equipment that have proved efficient for many of the commoner types of bend. Although it is not claimed that such equipment as is here illustrated is essential, or even the most efficient for specific purposes, it is hoped that the following information, which is of a practical nature, will be a guide to those who are not thoroughly acquainted with the practice of bending in general and will assist those who are desirous of modifying their present technique. Many of the methods and equipment described have been tested at the Laboratory, and much, therefore, of the following information is based on the experience so gained.

Cold Bending

The simplest type of bend may be said to be one made from untreated timber in its natural or dried state, but with few exceptions a comparatively small radius of curvature cannot be attained with such material without fracture occurring. For most wood, the limit is given by the formula $S/R = 0.02$ where S is the thickness of the piece and R the radius of curvature. Although this formula is by no means exact, it would indicate that a piece of wood 1 inch thick cannot be bent to a radius of much less than about 4 ft. in its natural state. Such a bent piece would be extremely elastic and could not be expected to set to shape so that it would need to be attached rigidly to some framework arranged roughly to the contour of the curve desired. Examples of this type may be found in the curved planking of boats which are sometimes cold bent and secured in place on the ribs. Where strength considerations are of little importance and only one face of a bent board is normally expected to be seen, the effective thickness of the piece may be reduced and bending in the cold state facilitated by removing portions from the concave face by means of kerf cuts. A series of transverse parallel saw cuts or grooves may be made on what is to be the inner face of the bend, which in effect reduce the thickness of the bent portion, thus reducing the limiting radius for fractureless bending and facilitating the operation generally. This method is frequently used by coffin manufacturers and by joiners in the fitting of curved rises to stairs, etc.

Hot Bending (Unsupported)

For bends of smaller radius, however, that are required to retain roughly their shape, the wood needs to be heat-softened in the manner already described. Good bending woods, such as beech and elm, may be bent to a much smaller radius of curvature after such treatment than before, even without the aid of straps. Some idea of the reduction in the limiting radius achieved as a result of steaming may be gathered from Table I, where it may be observed that for English beech, for example, the ratio of S to R now increases to a value of roughly 0.08. For making bends from steamed but unsupported material some such methods as the following are usually adopted :—

(1) The piece may be clamped between suitably curved male and female forms as shown in Fig. 6.

(2) The piece may be forced to shape over suitably prepared wooden, or preferably metal, forms and clamped in position in the manner shown in Fig. 7.

The male and female method (No. 1) has the disadvantage that difficulty is experienced in the drying and setting of the bent piece, and the second method is usually to be preferred.

Walking-sticks made from ash, cherry, blackthorn and other suitable wood may be bent, after heat treatment, around suitably curved forms by method No. 2, but the wedge or clamp may be replaced by a tie across the handle

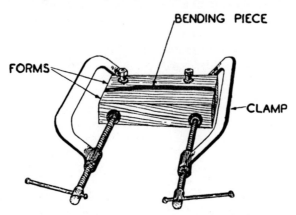

FIG. 6—*Bending between male and female forms*

if this has been bent through an angle of 180°. A bend so tied and held can be removed from the form for quick setting. It is interesting to note that if the bark is to remain on the stick it is essential to air-dry the wood before bending, and that it is by softening and bending the wood that initial curvature and twists in the piece as cut can be removed. There are many specific applications of the method of bending steamed but unsupported timber as,

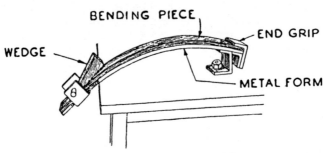

FIG. 7—*Bending over a metal form*

for example, in the ship-building trade where planking is made from boards steamed and bent manually to shape and secured to the ribs. One other special application only need be dealt with here, however, which, in effect, is a combination of hand and machine bending. A method frequently employed for the production of hoops for such articles as sieves, kettle-drums, barrels, etc., and found to be very satisfactory, consists of bending a thin strip of steamed material to a diameter smaller than that actually required, by means of a hand-operated machine resembling a mangle, Fig. 8. This machine consists essentially of two rollers which can be revolved by means of a hand wheel, and to one of the rollers is attached a steel band of approximately 18 S.W.G. After inserting one end of the steamed strip, which has already been cut to length and, if necessary, scarfed at the ends, between the metal band and the roller to which it is held, the machine is set in motion and the strip and band are wound on to the roller. On completion of this pre-bending operation, which should be carried out as rapidly as possible, the strip is immediately withdrawn from the machine, held by hand from uncoiling or, if necessary, re-coiled and forced inside a metal hoop. The inner diameter of this hoop is equal to the outer one of the wooden hoop or rim required. The scarfed ends of the strip are finally joined together with small nails and the whole removed from the metal ring to accelerate the setting and drying process.

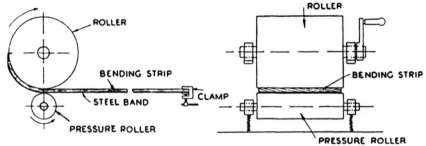

FIG. 8—*Bending hoops*

The diameter of the rollers in the first operation will depend on various factors such as, for instance, species and thickness of material to be bent, final shape required, etc. In general, therefore, it will be necessary to carry out a few preliminary experiments, but as a guide it may be stated that home-grown ash $\frac{7}{16}$ inch thick can successfully be bent into hoops of 14 inches internal diameter by this method when the diameter of the rollers is 9 inches. It should also be noted that any tendency for the wood to fracture during the first bending operation may be very considerably reduced by clamping together the metal band and specimen at the ends remote from the rollers, and such a procedure is to be recommended.

Hot Bending (Supported)

When the thickness of piece and radius of curvature are such that supporting straps are necessary to prevent fractures occurring on the stretched outer face, these straps are usually made of mild or spring steel. As a rough guide, a strap made of 18 S.W.G. steel should prove suitable for bends up to about $1\frac{1}{2}$ inches thick, and 14 S.W.G. for any thicker material. Spring steel is used when the nature of the bend is such as to make it necessary for the strap to be twisted as well as bent. A hard, brittle steel should be avoided, as it is unsuitable and dangerous for the operator. The width of strap should always be slightly greater than the width of wood, and all parts of the piece that is to be bent should be fully covered and supported.

If oak or other woods that are likely to stain in contact with steel have to be bent it is advisable to line the inner side of the strap with a thin sheet of aluminium, or other suitable material, which can be bent loosely over the edges of the strap to hold it in place. Various methods of attaching the steel strap to the wood are employed, but by far the best is to provide the strap with wooden or metal blocks, usually referred to as end-stops, and to fix or adjust these so that in the process of bending, the ends of the wood bear tightly on to them.

The forms around which the wood is to be bent may be made of wood or metal, the former being employed extensively for the simpler types of bends and where the number of bends of any one shape required is limited. Metal forms are usually employed for the production of complicated shapes and where a very large number of bends of the one shape are required. The advantages of using a metal form are that intermediate clamping is simplified, and the bend will not lose its shape if it becomes necessary to dry and set it while clamped in position.

Simple " U " Bend

In producing the common U-shaped bend it is usual first to locate and secure the mid-section of the wood and strap on the form and then to bend the two halves simultaneously around the form.

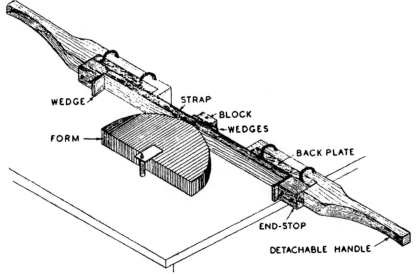

FIG. 9—*Initial set-up for making a simple U-shaped bend*

The initial set-up for making such a bend in this manner is shown in Fig. 9 where it will be seen that the bending form is clamped in position on a table and the steamed specimen and strap located and secured to it by means of blocks and wedges. Air clamps or other suitable device may, of course, be used in place of the system of wedges shown. It will be noted that the strap here is made taut initially by inserting wooden wedges between the ends of the specimen and the end-stops, but this is not always necessary as a small movement between wood and strap is often permissible and sometimes desirable. The bending operation is carried out by pulling the arms round to the final position shown in Fig. 10. It will be observed that the strap is fitted at both ends with back-plates which extend some distance along the back of the strap and are secured firmly to the end-stops. These usually take the form of flat plates of metal or wood strong enough to counteract any tendency for the end-stops to rotate when pressure is applied.

Without these plates the longitudinal forces transmitted by the wood to the strap tend to cause the end stops to swivel in the manner illustrated in Fig. 11. This may result in the wood freeing itself from the strap or, if prevented from doing this by the pull on the handles, it will most probably back bend in the manner shown. The importance of providing bending straps with some form of back-plate can hardly be overstressed, and troubles encountered in practice are frequently attributable to their omission. The completed bend is held in

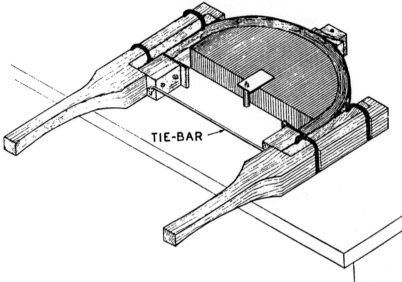

TIE-BAR

FIG. 10—*Completion of bending operation with tie-bar attached*

position either by hand or, preferably, by means of a clamp while some suitable tie-bar is being fixed across the ends to hold them in place for setting and drying. A convenient clamping device for the temporary holding of the bend to the form consists of air clamps, the tops of which are flush with the table top during the bending operation and which may be caused to rise upward immediately behind the strap at the conclusion of the operation, thus holding the ends in position. In the arrangement shown, Fig. 10, the tie-bar used takes the form of a metal rod bent at the ends so as to fit in to eye-bolts secured to the centre of the back end of the end-stops. The handles on the ends of the strap are removable so that once the tie-bar is in position the bend, complete with strap, end-stops, back-plates and tie-bar, can be removed from the form for setting in the manner illustrated in Fig. 12.

For many bends of this type it may be found unnecessary to keep the strap in position during drying and setting, though the tendency for fractures to develop during this period is thereby considerably increased. It will still, however, be necessary to tie the ends of the bend, and this may be done by nailing wooden strips across them, or by some such similar device. It will be necessary to nail strips both to the top and the bottom of the bent piece to overcome any tendency for the bend to twist on removal of the strap. Apart from the increased tendency for the bend to fracture in drying by removing the strap in this manner, the ends of the piece often are damaged as the result of nailing, and if more than one piece is to be bent in the one operation it becomes virtually impossible to secure strips on the top and bottom of each before removal of the strap, so that twisting is almost sure to result.

If the shape of the bend is not symmetrical, it will probably be found that on removal from the form appreciable change of shape will immediately take place when the simple forms of tie-bars already described are used. In such cases, it becomes necessary to clamp the bend to the form and remove the complete assembly to the drying-room for setting.

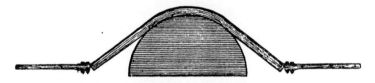

(a) Bend made without back plates showing the tendency to swivel.

(b) Bend made with back plates too short to be effective.

(c) Satisfactory bend made with extended back plates.

Fig. 11—*Bending with and without back plates*

When the piece to be bent is of small cross-section as compared with its length, there is always a tendency for the parts of the wood not yet in contact with the form to flex and bend away from the strap owing to the longitudinal pressure induced. As a result of this " snaking " or " back-bending," fractures are very liable to occur, and the finished bend will most likely be out of plane and distorted. It has already been explained that some of this tendency can be counteracted by the use of back-plates, but these alone are not always sufficient. A further method of minimizing such troubles is to allow the wood surface in contact with the strap to stretch a limited and controlled amount. This stretch must never be allowed to exceed about 2 per cent of the total length bent, as otherwise tension failures will be present on the finished bend.

Such control may be obtained by providing the strap with adjustable end-stops such, for instance, as the one shown in Fig. 13. With an end-stop of this type, the strap can be made to fit tightly on the wood at the commencement of the bend and the pressures controlled during bending by means of the hand-operated adjustment screw. Yet another method, whereby back-

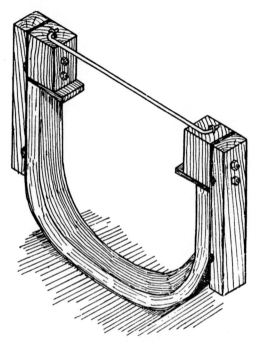

FIG. 12—*Bend ready for removal to setting chamber*

bending or inadvertent distortions can be minimized, is by the use of vertical and horizontal clamps (Fig. 14), but unless proved to be absolutely necessary, such additional equipment should obviously be avoided if production rate is to be maintained as high as possible. End-stops are not usually left on this type

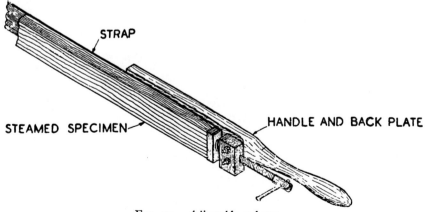

FIG. 13—*Adjustable end-stop*

of bend during the setting period, and if the completed bend is such that the strap cannot safely be removed and the support it offers dispensed with immediately, without fear of fracture on the convex face, it will be advantageous to make the end-stop detachable. It is, however, important to keep these

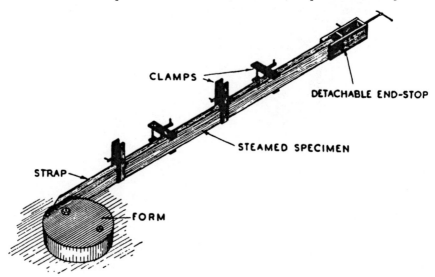

FIG. 14—*Initial set-up of strap, clamps and adjustable end-stop for ring seat type bend*

end-stops in position until a few fixing and holding clamps have been tightly fitted, as otherwise the strap may slip along the wood, causing tension failures to occur on the bend. Two types of adjustable and detachable end-stops are shown in Figs. 15 and 16.

Two-plane Bends

For bends that are to be made in more than one plane, the straps used have necessarily to be arranged so that the bent parts of the wood are always covered on the convex face, irrespective of the plane of bending. A strap made on these lines is shown in Fig. 17 placed in position on a wood specimen prior to bending in two planes.

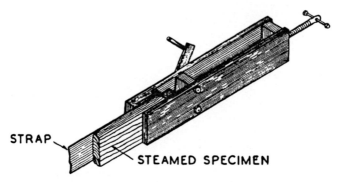

FIG. 15—*Detachable and adjustable end-stop*

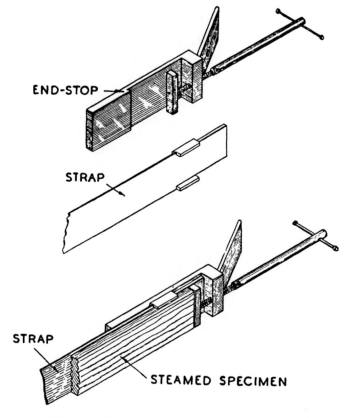

END-STOP

STRAP

STRAP

STEAMED SPECIMEN

Fig. 16—*Detachable and adjustable end-stop*

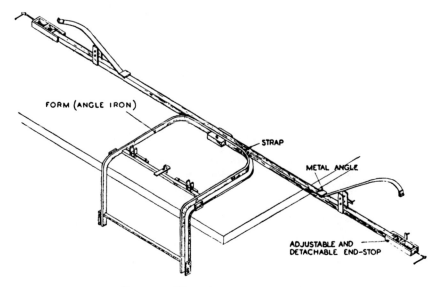

FORM (ANGLE IRON)

STRAP

METAL ANGLE

ADJUSTABLE AND
DETACHABLE END-STOP

Fig. 17—*Two-plane bend (initial set-up)*

The first part of such a bend is effected in the normal manner, making use, if necessary, of intermediate clamps to minimize the risk of back-bending and to keep the wood within the limits of the strap.

As soon as this part is completed it is clamped to the form and the end-stops removed. It is important to keep these end-stops in position until the fixing clamps are really tight, as otherwise the strap may slip along the wood, causing tension failures to occur on the bends. The two loose pieces of strap at right angles, and secured by metal angles to the main strap, are next put in position along the wood, and the released end-stops fitted to their ends. These straps are pulled tight by manipulation of the end screw, and the two ends of the wood can then safely be bent in a plane at right angles to the centre part, Fig. 18. Intermediate clamps may, or may not be needed along the strap,

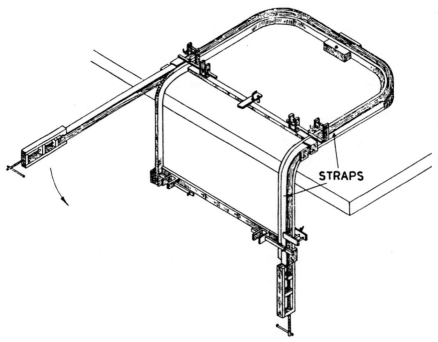

FIG. 18—*Final stages in making a two-plane bend*

according to the nature of the wood, its dimensions, etc., but the finished bend is usually left clamped to the form and dried and set in this state.

A somewhat simpler, but effective, strapping arrangement for making bends in two planes is shown in Fig. 19. Here the centre portion only of the back strap is made of continuous steel strip to which, as before, metal angles are attached to the ends. The end portions consist, however, of a series of short metal strips linked one to another so as to be free to swivel in the vertical plane. The end-stop is not detachable and is not usually adjustable. The secondary straps used for supporting the bend during the second part of the operation are secured to the metal angles on the ends of the centre portion of the main back strap and also to the front of the end-stops. When the first part of the bend has been made and firmly clamped to the form, the end portions can immediately be bent in a plane at right angles to the centre

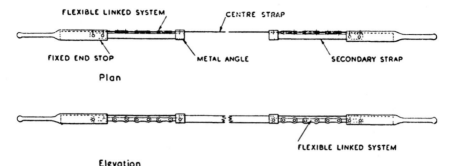

FLEXIBLE LINKED SYSTEM   CENTRE STRAP

FIXED END STOP   METAL ANGLE   SECONDARY STRAP

Plan

FLEXIBLE LINKED SYSTEM

Elevation

FIG. 19—*Strap with flexible linked system for making a two-plane bend*

portion, since the secondary straps are already in position and the linked ends of the main strap are able to adjust themselves to the curvature imposed in this direction. Since it is advisable to set the finished bends clamped to the form, metal forms are to be preferred to wood for most types of two-plane bends.

Re-entrant and S-type Bends

In producing a bend in the form of an S it is usually necessary to secure two straps simultaneously to the piece to be bent, one to support one convex face and one to support the other. One method of making such a bend is to secure the forms to a baseplate in their correct relative positions and to fix to each a separate strap. Each strap is fitted with an end-stop, and the piece to be bent is laid in between, as shown in Fig. 20. The two ends are bent simultaneously and secured in position on the forms until dried and set. A variation

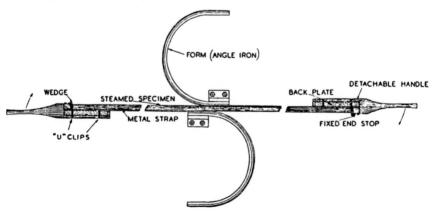

FORM (ANGLE IRON)

WEDGE   STEAMED SPECIMEN   BACK PLATE   DETACHABLE HANDLE

"U" CLIPS   METAL STRAP   FIXED END STOP

FIG. 20—" S " *type of bend*

of this method is to fit two long straps, one on either side of the piece, and to use these alternately, as depicted in Fig. 21. Detachable end-stops are here essential, and after each part of the bend is made it is clamped securely between forms prior to the removal of the end-stop and the subsequent bending in the reverse direction. Re-entrant bends can be made by this method and a sinuous type bend may be produced if the process is continued. Where the re-entrant bend is of comparatively large radius of curvature it is often possible

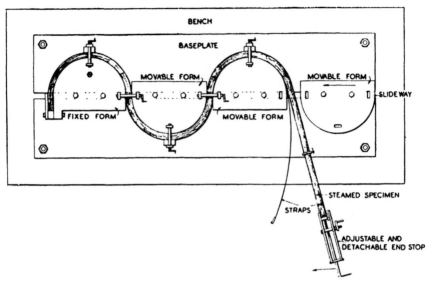

FIG. 21—*A method of making a sinuous type bend*

to make it between male and female forms in the manner shown in Fig. 22. A bending strap is provided for the bends of smaller radius yet to be made, and this may be clamped between the specimen and the male form. As soon as the first part of the bend has been produced and the forms, wood and strap tightly clamped together, the end-stops on the strap are fitted to the ends of the specimen and these are respectively bent in the normal manner. Here again it will be necessary to remove the complete set-up for drying and setting.

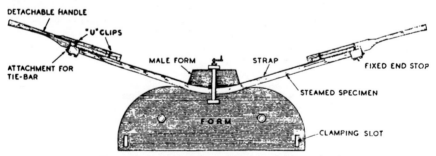

FIG. 22—*A method of making a re-entrant bend*

Chair Leg Bends

Bends of comparatively large radius of curvature, suitable for chair legs, may be bent unsupported over metal forms in the manner already described, but when the curvature is such as to lead to fractures in bending it is necessary to provide the piece with a supporting strap. An arrangement such as that shown in Fig. 23 is a very suitable one for this purpose.

A variation of this method, employing a steam-heated form for quick setting, is shown in Plate 7.

One of the most complicated types of bend is that usually associated with the legs and back of the well-known Austrian bentwood chairs. Such bends often

PLATE 9—Bending wood by means of a winch

PLATE 10—Chain type lever arm bending machine

PLATE 11—Lever arm bending machine operated by a rack and pinion mechanism

PLATE 12—Revolving table bending machine

PLATE 13—Hydraulic press and steam-heated cauls

PLATE 14—Hand-operated bending machine

PLATE 15—Spade handle bending machine

PLATE 16—Bending machine for making split type spade handles

are, in effect, a combination of the two-plane bend and the re-entrant. The straps used for these may resemble those used for the two-plane bend already referred to, and intermediate clamping devices are frequently employed. Normally, the back or top part is first bent to shape and tightly clamped to the form before any attempt is made to bend the legs proper. One leg is then bent at a time and two men are required for the operation. Experience alone teaches the operators just where to place the intermediate clamps and when to remove them, and, indeed, success depends here almost as much upon correct clamping as upon other factors.

The set-up of such a bend just prior to the bending of the second half is shown in Plate 8.

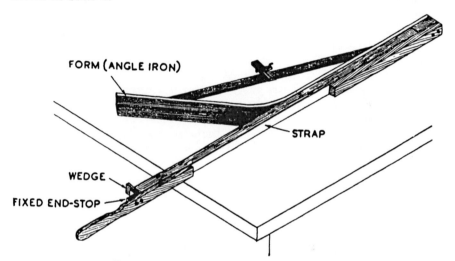

FORM (ANGLE IRON)

STRAP

WEDGE

FIXED END-STOP

FIG. 23—*A method of making a chair leg bend*

By means of such clamps as are illustrated in the photograph the several portions of the strap are held in their correct place on the wood, so that with a pre-adjustment of end-pressure, tension failures may be avoided. Some reduction of pressure may be necessary during bending.

The bend here depicted is made of square-sectioned beech, but round-sectioned wood can also be bent in like manner ; clamp marking and flattening of such pieces are, however, often serious. A round-sectioned bend can also be made by means of one continuous flexible steel strap twisted around the piece and held with clamps in such a manner as to keep the convex faces of bent parts well covered. The forms, which should be of metal, should be painted with aluminium paint or galvanized to avoid staining the wood, and if the strap is not of stainless steel a thin strip of aluminium, or similar material, should be placed between it and the wood.

Transverse Bending

It is not always realized that almost all woods may readily be bent in the transverse direction across the grain. Unfortunately, however, wood is fissile and very prone to fracture when subjected to tensile stress across the fibres, and in making bends of small radii of curvature in this direction some support for the convex face is required.

3—23841

As an example of the possibilities of this method it may be stated that a wood such as spruce, which is considered to have inferior bending properties when bent with the grain, may be bent across the grain without a strap, after immersion in boiling water, into the form of a tube having an internal diameter of $3\frac{1}{2}$ inches and a wall thickness of $\frac{1}{8}$ inch.

One method employed for making such a tube has been to clamp one edge of the panel to a heated steam pipe and then to steam the face remote from the pipe so as to cause the piece to curve around it. After sufficient treatment, a strip of strong cloth or canvas is placed over the convex face to afford some mechanical support, and the whole slowly bent around the heated pipe until the required shape has been obtained. It remains then to dry and set the bend before removing it from the pipe.

Steamed wood can be heavily compressed across the fibres without fracturing, and the forces set up in bending are comparatively small.

Another example of cross-grained bending is shown in Plate 4, which illustrates a bend made with Scots pine 1 inch thick around a form radius of 3 inches. In making this bend the wood was steamed and the convex face fully supported by means of a wide steel strap. In view of the inherent weakness of cross-grain bends and their instability, the method appears to have been confined to date to the production of laminated material in a manner such as is to be described and illustrated later.

CHAPTER IV

MACHINE BENDING

Rope and Windlass Machine

IN whatever manner wood is bent, the principles underlying the process remain the same, but by the use of machinery, as distinct from the comparatively simple hand-bending equipment, a large number of bends may often be made in one operation, and the bending of large-dimensioned stock greatly facilitated. Strictly it might be said that the extended levers or handles fitted to the straps used in hand-bending methods constitute machines or multiplying devices whereby greater forces may be exerted on the wood than would otherwise be possible. It is not usual, however, to regard them in this light and such equipment is seldom used for the production of multiple bends or bends of large dimensions. Probably the simplest form of bending machine in the true sense consists of a hand- or power-driven winch linked by means of ropes or chains to the ends of the bending straps in the manner illustrated in Plate 9.

For the initial set-up, the bending form is clamped to a bench, and to the vertex of this form is clamped the mid-section of the wood-strap system. In the arrangement shown, the strap is of simple design, fitted with wooden end-stops and back-plates. Wooden wedges have been inserted between the steamed bending blanks and the end-stops for the tightening of the strap. Guide pulleys are fitted along the length of bench joining the form and winch, and these are located in such a position that the ropes which pass around them exert a pull as nearly at right angles to the end-stops throughout the bending operation as is possible. By the operation of the winch, the two ends of the strap may then be pulled forward and towards one another so that the wood is caused to be wrapped tightly around the form.

In the particular set-up shown, the bend, when completed, was clamped securely to the form with the strap in position and the whole assembly removed to a drying room for the " setting " of the wood. The final drying would be accomplished with the strap removed, and wooden tie pieces nailed across the ends of each bend.

The alternative arrangement of fitting ropes or metal tie-bars so as to connect the ends of the strap as soon as the bend has been made might have been adopted in preference to securing with clamps.

Lever Arm Machines

The so-called lever arm machines are essentially the same as the one already described, except that they are provided with stout metal levers or arms, by means of which the forces are transmitted to the wood-strap system.

A machine of this type is shown in Plate 10, and its similarity with the machine already described is readily apparent. The framework for this type of machine is usually vertical, and the guide pulleys, over which pass the ropes or chains operating the arms, are normally situated near the top. These chains are connected at one end to a power-driven winch, and at the other are secured to the ends of the lever arms in a manner such as that shown.

A strong metal strap, referred to commonly as the major strap, is placed over the top faces of the metal lever arms and is secured to each at its ends.

In addition to the major strap, strong adjustable end-stop fittings are attached, one to each arm, and arrangements made so that these may be clamped in several different positions along the lengths of the arms so that the distances apart may correspond with the lengths of the pieces to be bent. The ends of the arms, not supported by chains or ropes, are provided with hinged metal supports. To the lower end of these are fitted metal rollers. These rollers are mounted on horizontal grooved rails or channels, the height of which in a commercial machine would be made adjustable. The fit of the rollers into the groove or channel is such that lengthwise movement is not impeded, but lateral or rotational movement is inhibited.

Spring-loaded wire ropes are attached to the roller ends of the metal supports, so that forces may thus be applied tending to pull the rollers in towards one another. The bending form is bolted in place along the centre line of the frame and, in the initial set-up, the length of the chains, the height of the rails, and the forces in the springs, are so adjusted that the lever arms are in one horizontal line at a distance below the bottom of the form sufficient to allow the steamed wood specimen or specimens to be inserted between the form and strap. Before the wood is inserted in position, a minor strap, with metal angles or plates secured to its ends, is placed snugly in position between the two strong major end-stops.

The wood and protecting straps, once in position, are clamped to the lowest point on the form in a manner similar to that shown in Plate 10.

It remains now to set the winch in operation for the arms, wood and straps to be pulled upward and around the form until the wood has assumed the shape required. At the conclusion of the bending operation, a tie-bar or hook may be fitted across the ends of the minor strap so as to secure the wood and protecting minor strap in its final position on the form. Pressure on the adjustable major end-stops is released by manipulation of adjusting screws, with which they are normally provided, and the arms returned once again to the horizontal position. The fixing clamp is next released, and the wood, with minor strap in position, removed for the setting of the bend.

A rather neater and somewhat more compact machine of the lever arm type is shown in Plate 11. In this model there are, in effect, two arms on either side of the centre line, and the top pair, to which is fitted the major strap, is

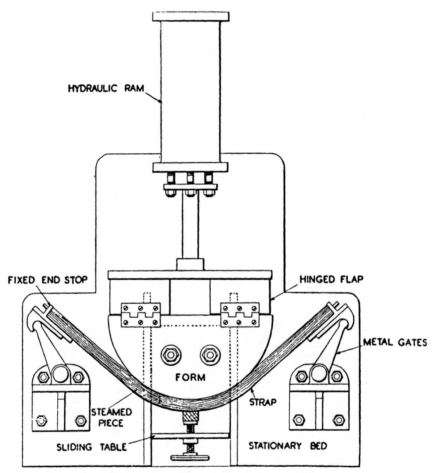

FIG. 24—*A bending machine incorporating a hydraulic ram*

connected to the bottom pair by means of struts pivoted top and bottom, as shown in the illustration. The power unit is coupled directly with the lower pair of arms through a rack and pinion mechanism, and the forces are transmitted to the upper pair by the pivoted links.

In all other essentials, this machine and the one already described are similar, and the method of operation is to all intents and purposes the same.

A modification of the above method is illustrated in plan in Fig. 24, in which arrangement the bending form is caused to move towards the wood, and end-stop movement takes place mainly in a lateral direction.

The framework consists essentially of (*a*) a stationary bed and (*b*) a sliding table free to move backwards and forwards along grooves in the stationary bed.

The bending form is secured to the sliding table and movement is imparted to it by means of a pneumatic or hydraulic ram.

On the fixed bed are fitted two stout metal hinges or gates of suitable dimensions, and at a distance apart approximately equal to the length of the wood to be bent. The metal straps used are equipped with fixed end-stops and with metal back-plates extending slightly beyond the end-stops. On the backs of these plates, near their extremities, are cut semi-circular grooves which fit snugly on to the rounded ends of the metal gates on the stationary bed.

In the initial set-up, the ram is at the back of its stroke, the wood is in position between the end-stops of the strap, and the rounded ends of the metal gates are fitted into the grooves of the back-plate.

The bending form is now forced forward by the ram into the wood and, since the ends of the strap are constrained to move only in the arc of a circle, the wood-strap system is forced eventually to take up the shape of the form when the bending operation is completed.

It remains then to secure the ends of the strap by means of a tie-bar, withdraw the form slightly and remove the tied bend, complete with strap, from the form for setting.

Revolving Table Machine

In this type of machine, one end of the wood and one of the steel strap are attached to a point on or near the bending form, which, in turn, is secured to a table or disc that can be rotated at will. A spring-loaded roller bears upon the back of the wood and strap at the point of contact with the form. To this roller is attached a long metal slide or feed arm along which the end-stop remote from the form is constrained to move. When the table is revolved the wood and strap are automatically wrapped around the form and kept in close contact by the pressure exerted radially by the roller. Such a machine, used for making complete rings for chair seats, etc., is shown in Plate 12.

In this type of machine the sliding end-stop is usually made adjustable and detachable, and it is not customary to have both a major and a minor strap, as one strap alone is sufficient. For making complete hoops or bends of over 360° no end-plate or angle is fitted to the strap, and it is necessary to clamp the end of the strap to the wood before removing the sliding end-stop from the strap and hence the bend from the table. In the machine illustrated end pressure during bending may be controlled by means of a hand wheel and screw fitted to the sliding end-stop, but, in addition, automatic pressure reduction can be obtained by means of a wedge and inclined plane mechanism incorporated in the design.

When a machine of this type is employed for making U-type bends it is usual to provide the strap with metal plates or angles somewhat similar to those of the minor strap used in the lever arm type machine.

With such an arrangement, the plunger of the adjustable end-stop can be made to pass through a slot in the angle and so take the end thrust of the wood until the bend is complete.

The operation of the plunger during the bend is again such that the wood can stretch a limited and regulated amount until it comes into contact with the end angle of the strap. This point should be reached just before the bend is completed, so that finally, when a connecting bar is placed in position, the plunger may be withdrawn and the adjustable end-stop apparatus completely detached from the strap.

Machines of this type are capable of producing almost every bend that can be made on the lever arm type machine and, in addition, there is no limit to the angle of bend. The disadvantages of this type as compared with the lever arm are, first, that by starting the bend from one end, as distinct from starting near the middle, the time taken is almost doubled and, secondly, that there is an increased tendency for such parts of the wood as are not in contact with the form to bend upwards or sideways. This " back-bending " may be a serious feature when the specimen is long in comparison with its cross-sectional dimensions, and can only be overcome by reducing the end-pressures to a minimum by suitable manipulation of the end-stop or by clamping the wood and strap together at intermediate points.

Presses

Steamed wood is sometimes pressed to shape between male and female dies or cauls. Should a large hydraulic press be used in conjunction with a series of cauls, a considerable number of bends may be pressed in one operation and the whole battery may be clamped together and removed for " setting ".

Sometimes the press is provided with steam-heated cauls for quick setting, and such a press is illustrated in Plate 13. In such a set-up the bent pieces are left in the press until set to shape.

If, as in the illustration, no supporting straps are used, the limiting radius of curvature must be comparatively large and great accuracy of shape cannot be obtained. It is, of course, quite possible to provide the wood with supporting straps if required, and an excellent set-up of this kind for bending chair back posts has been described and fully illustrated by Thomas R. C. Wilson of the Forest Products Laboratory, Madison, U.S.A.[*]

A very simple hand-operated machine used for making the top bends of chair backs is illustrated in Plate 14.

The bending forms or cauls here are made of wood, and a metal strap has been introduced, as the radius of curvature is smaller than the limiting radius for unsupported material.

The tie-rods used consist of metal bars bent at the ends and pointed. A pair of these is driven into the ends of the bent piece to hold it roughly to shape, after the strap has been removed and during setting.

Spade Handle Bending Machines

Finally, mention may be made of machines commonly used for bending the ends of spade and shovel handles.

These are illustrated in Plates 15 and 16, and they consist essentially of a fixed clamp for holding one end of the spade handle and a metal form arranged so as to slide freely along guides in the framework of the machine.

Split forms are used, and the top half is kept in contact with the bottom during the bending operation by means of a wedge clamp. The top half of each form is slightly deeper than the bottom, and all are grooved and shaped to the required contour of the finished bend. The end of the handle to be bent is first softened by immersion in boiling water, after which the handle is securely gripped and held in a horizontal position by the stationary fixing clamp. The sliding form is then driven forward by a power-driven cam or other suitable mechanism and the softened wood forced into the appropriately shaped grooves provided in the form.

Finally, the fixing clamp is released, the wedge clamp removed, and the top half of the form, complete with the bent portion of the wood now fitting closely inside it, taken to a warm room, or placed over steam-heated pipes, for the setting of the wood to shape. As soon as the bent portion has re-dried and set, the upper half of the metal form is disengaged, and the operation completed.

As might be expected, fractures are not uncommon with this somewhat violent method of unsupported bending but, fortunately, considerable tolerance is permissible in regard to such fractures as may occur.

Cooperage

The art of making tight casks or barrels for holding liquids is one of great antiquity, demanding the greatest skill and care since, in addition to being perfectly leak-proof, the vessels must bear the strain of transportation, and in many cases they have to resist considerable internal pressure when they contain fermenting liquors. There are, of course, several types of barrels for holding a variety of liquids, and the species of timber used and methods employed for their manufacture are not all the same. For example, in the herring industry, softwood staves are commonly used and made ready for bending by heating over a wood fire. In the brewing industry, however, steam is now used to an increasing extent for the softening process, and machinery commonly employed for the actual bending operation.

Probably one of the most important operations in making barrels is the shaping of the staves, which in the brewing industry are usually made from well-seasoned quartered oak and are so fashioned that finally it is only necessary to bend them in one direction to obtain the shape of the barrel. Each stave is usually machined to exact profile and has an increase of width from the ends to the middle, a bevel on each edge, and is curved on the faces which finally form the inner and outer sides of the finished barrel.

In the process of assembly a number of staves are selected and these, one by one, are stood on end and their top ends fitted within a metal hoop. When a sufficient number of staves have been arranged in this manner another hoop of larger diameter is slipped over the assembly and forced along the staves, drawing them tighter together so that at this stage the assembly resembles roughly a truncated cone with the bottom ends of the staves splayed outwards.

The assembly of staves with the two hoops in position is then taken to a steaming box, which may consist of a base-plate fitted with an open-ended steam pipe and a bell-shaped metal top of rather larger dimensions than the stave assembly. The metal top or hood can be raised well clear of the base-plate so as to accommodate the assembly, which is placed over the centrally situated steam pipe. As soon as the top is lowered so as to form a reasonably steam-tight chest, the steam is turned on and the staves subjected to a suitable softening treatment. Immediately after the treatment, the assembly is removed to a bending machine which frequently consists essentially of a rope and windlass and some mechanism for forcing into position additional metal hoops. The rope is wrapped around the splayed bottom ends of the staves in such a way that when tightened by means of the windlass, these ends are pulled inwards and drawn together. Metal hoops of varying diameters are then, one by one, placed over the assembly and forced into position mechanically, thus binding and forcing the staves still tighter together until the required size of barrel has been obtained. Once the strain is taken by the hoops, the rope may be released, and it then remains to cool and dry the wood for the proper setting of the staves to shape. Other operations connected with the fitting of the heads, permanent hoops, etc., are finally carried out before the barrel is completed, but these are not concerned with bending *per se* and are therefore beyond the scope of the present work.

CHAPTER V

THE "SETTING" OF BENDS

IT has been shown in a previous chapter that during the bending process tensile and compressive strains are induced in the material and that unless these are kept within certain limits they may cause fractures to occur. Residual stresses in the bent material unless held in restraint will cause a piece of bent wood to open out and return approximately to its former shape. If, for example, the clamps or tie-bars holding a bend to shape are removed immediately after the bending operation, movement of the ends of the bend in an outward direction will almost invariably occur. The distance moved will depend on several factors, such as the moisture content and species of the bend, radius of curvature, etc., and such movement will continue until the residual forces are of insufficient magnitude to overcome the stiffness of the piece as a whole. During the bending process the material is usually strained beyond its elastic limit, some permanent deformation of the fibres occurs and for this reason seldom does a piece so bent, if allowed to move, return completely to its former shape. When, however, the induced strains are below the elastic limit, removal of all restraint will result in almost complete removal of the strain in the fibres and hence the piece will return very nearly to its original shape.

In order, therefore, to cause a piece of bent wood to retain its curvature it is essential either to reduce the magnitude of the latent stresses causing movement, or increase the stiffness, or employ a combination of the two. This process is referred to as the "setting" of bends, but it does not follow that because a bend is "set" to shape it is necessarily perfectly dry and ready for incorporation in the finished article.

Setting can be accomplished most readily by removing some of the moisture and by cooling the bent piece, and in some respects may be considered as a reversal of the softening treatment when the wood is heated under moist conditions. Though moisture is probably the factor of greatest importance in the setting process, it is not necessary that a bend should be dried down to any particular moisture content before becoming "set". In fact, when green timber has been used in making a bend it may subsequently be found after cooling to be set approximately to the shape of the form on which it was made, even though the moisture content of the bend after the setting process is still high and on the average even in excess of the fibre saturation value.

Since, ideally, before a bend is incorporated in the finished product it should be both "set" and dried to the appropriate moisture content in service, it is apparent that further drying of such bends after the setting process becomes necessary. This further drying will be accompanied by a change in shape of the bend as will be explained later. When, therefore, accuracy of shape is essential, it is recommended that the bend should first be set, then conditioned in the workshop and finally machined to exact profile.

The setting process may be considerably accelerated by subjecting the bend to hot, dry air, and in many instances temperatures as high as 150-160° F. can be used without damage being caused. Setting rooms are usually designed after the fashion of a simple drying-kiln incorporating steam-heated pipes, although any warm store would be equally suitable for the purpose, especially if provision is made for removing the moist air. It is seldom necessary to control the air humidity in a setting room.

During the setting process a bend must always be held to shape, and if removed from the bending form must be held by means of nailed strips, tie-bars or other similar attachments. In some instances it may be found safe to remove the strap immediately after the bending operation, but usually when a bend is hot and wet it then becomes very liable to fail subsequently in tension even though faultless when removed from the bending form. Straps, if possible, should therefore be left on the bend for part of, if not all of, the setting period and should preferably not be removed until the bend has cooled and been out of the setting room for an hour or so.

No definite periods of setting can be given as these will depend on several factors, such as room temperature, size and moisture content of stock, etc., and it will generally be found necessary to carry out a few preliminary tests to determine the most suitable period for any particular bend. A very rough indication of how far setting has advanced may, however, usually be obtained by visiting the setting room at intervals and testing the tightness of clamps, tie bars, etc. When these are loose to the touch it may be assumed that the bend is set. As a rough guide, it may be said that $1\frac{1}{4}$- × $1\frac{1}{4}$-inch air-dried English oak bent to a radius of 9 inches may be set at a temperature of 150° F. in some 9 hours, and if then removed from the straps and placed for conditioning in a room at, say, 75° F. should be ready for use in about two weeks.

Bends made from green oak may be set in a similar manner but, as already explained, considerable risks attend such a process, and a very long time must necessarily elapse before the wood is thoroughly conditioned. Lower setting temperatures can, of course, be used and in certain cases are to be recommended, as when, for example, strength characteristics of the finished product are of paramount importance, or the material is likely to collapse or in any other way suffer from the rapid drying at higher temperatures.

Sometimes bent wood components, especially in small cross-sectional dimensions, can be incorporated in a finished article before they are fully dried without causing serious trouble in use, but the extent to which such deviation from the ideal is permissible is a matter for the practical man to decide from his own experience. Finally, it should be noted that when the strains induced in making a bend are largely within the elastic limit of the material, as in bends of comparatively large radii of curvature, such bends tend nearly always to straighten out somewhat when freed from restraint, even though thoroughly dried. It is usual, therefore, initially to bend such pieces to a rather smaller radius than that required, and so allow for such subsequent alteration in curvature. Furthermore, in view of the difficulty of holding certain bends of large radius to shape during the setting process, it is preferable to make and set them on heated metal forms in the manner already described.

The Movement or Change in Shape of Bends

Bends of comparatively small radius do not open out to the same extent when dried and, in fact, bends of very small radius frequently turn inwards when released, owing to the natural shrinkages that have occurred during drying. If the bend has been thoroughly dried, it will take up its final position as soon as it is freed from restraint, and subsequent movements will not necessarily be appreciable unless it is subjected to abnormal changes in atmospheric conditions. Fluctuating atmospheric conditions affect bent wood rather more than a piece cut to shape, for not only are there the same consequent changes in cross-sectional dimensions which in themselves account for changes in the radius of curvature, but also longitudinally compressed wood shows an increased tendency to shrink and expand in the longitudinal direction. An increase in moisture content will cause the radius to increase, and similarly a decrease will cause the radius to decrease. There is also a latent tendency for a bend to straighten out, and if it is subjected to high humidity conditions for a long period it may open out considerably and not return exactly to its original shape and curvature when re-dried. If the bend becomes very wet indeed, particularly at high temperatures, it may open out very appreciably if unsupported, and if held at the ends it may actually break. Such troubles are not common in this country, but are not infrequent in tropical climates where every effort should be made to render the bends as impervious to moisture as possible and keep them dry by artificial means in so far as this can be done.

Part II

LAMINATED BENDING

CHAPTER VI

THE PROCESS OF LAMINATED BENDING

IT is well known that all timbers can be bent to a certain extent in the cold state without fracturing, and that very thin strips may easily be bent to a small radius of curvature. Pieces so bent, however, owing to their elastic properties, will tend to resume their original shape upon removal of the bending forces unless they are secured and held to shape in some way. Such support or fixing may be afforded by firmly securing the bent pieces to a rigid framework or by securing one to another a number of concentrically bent pieces in such a manner that relative movements are rendered virtually impossible. This latter method is the one now to be considered and is usually referred to as the method of laminated bending. In this method thin wooden strips or laminæ are assembled one on top of the other like cards in a deck and all are bent simultaneously over a single bending form. No restraint is imposed on the ends of any one lamina, which is free to slide over a contiguous lamina during the bending process. The completed bend thus consists of a series of individually bent laminæ which are usually secured one upon the other by means of glue on contiguous faces. The individually bent laminæ are no longer free to slide over each other when the glue has set and relative movement is in this manner so restrained that virtually no further alteration in shape can occur, and the bend as a whole thus becomes set and fixed to shape.

The advantages of this method are that thick bends of small radius can be built up from thin laminæ of any species of timber whatsoever, and even poor quality timber containing knots, splits and other defects which would render the wood quite unfit for solid bending may, within reason, be incorporated.

If the laminæ are sliced or rotary cut, considerable saving in timber may be effected, but conversely, of course, considerable loss may be occasioned if thin laminæ are prepared by sawing. Long lengths may be obtained fairly readily by scarf-jointing laminæ end to end, and if these joints are staggered in the completed bend no very appreciable weakening of the cross section need result. Finally, laminated bends can usually be set more readily and made to conform better to the shape of the jig than similar bends of solid material. The disadvantages are : more technical skill and better equipment are usually required than for solid bending ; the presence of glue is somewhat detrimental to the machines used for the final cleaning up of the bent piece ; the glue lines which are usually visible on the sides are sometimes objected to for æsthetic reasons ; and the production of laminated bends in more than one plane presents greater difficulties than are encountered in the method of solid bending.

Selection and Preparation of Laminæ

In preparing laminæ for the production of laminated bends, the methods used are essentially the same as those used in making flat laminated assemblies. It is, however, particularly important when preparing laminæ for bent members to ensure that each individual lamina is of uniform thickness, since the methods normally employed in pressing together the glued laminæ do not permit the use of high pressures and any appreciable variation in thickness may result in glue-line fractures. Furthermore, no laminæ containing any form of decay should be used, as these will almost certainly be found to be extremely brittle. Laminæ should be dried to a moisture content of less than 20 per cent before they can be considered in a fit state for gluing, and they may be in the form of sawn, sliced or rotary cut veneers or plywood.

It is uncommon, except in the manufacture of structural members and ships' timbers, to incorporate laminæ much over ⅛ inch in thickness, but in selecting the thickness of laminæ to be used one of the most important factors to be considered is the limiting radius of curvature to which the wood can be bent without fractures occurring.

Some idea of the limiting radii of curvature of several different species of laminæ may be obtained by reference to Table II. This table has been

TABLE II*—*The Limiting Radii of Curvature of Various Species of Laminæ*

Species	Thickness of laminæ (Inches)	Average moisture content (Per cent)	Radius in inches at which losses due to breakages did not exceed 5 per cent of the pieces bent	Approximate ratio : radius/ thickness of laminæ
Beech (home-grown) (Fagus sylvatica)	0.125	13.0	4.4	35
Elm, Dutch (home-grown) (Ulmus hollandica var major)	0.125	13.0	3.9	31
Douglas fir .. .. (Pseudotsuga taxifolia)	0.10	13.2	8.5	85
Hemlock, Western .. (Tsuga heterophylla)	0.10	13.3	5.3	53
Oak (home-grown) .. (Quercus robur)	0.125	12.5	5.8	46
Spruce, Sitka .. .. (Picea sitchensis)	0.125	12.5	6.0	48
Spruce, Sitka .. .. (Picea sitchensis)	0.104	12.2	6.0	58
Spruce, Sitka .. .. (Picea sitchensis)	0.08	12.3	3.6	45

compiled from data obtained at the Forest Products Research Laboratory and indicates the " safe " radius of curvature to which certain laminæ may be bent so that only 5 per cent of the total number of bent pieces will fracture during the process. It needs to be added that the data in the table refer to good quality material free from all defects such as pin knots, etc., straight in the grain and bent in the cold dry state around unheated forms with the grain of each lamina at an angle of 90° to the axis of curvature. Further tests have yet to be carried out before any definite pronouncement can be made concerning the effect of other variables such, for example, as direction of the annual growth rings relative to the axis of curvature, method of conversion,

---

*See Supplement to Table II (pp. 69 and 70).

i.e. rotary or sawn, rate of growth, etc., on the limiting radii of curvature, but it appears probable that these factors have in general a negligible effect.

In general, laminæ obtained from hardwoods can be bent to smaller radii than laminæ of the same thickness obtained from softwoods. Furthermore, when sliced or rotary-cut veneers are used in bends, if fractures are to be avoided, it is important to ensure that the " loose " face of the material is on the concave face of the bend, or in other words that it is in compression during the bending process. The effect that the position of the " loose " face has on the limiting radii of curvature may be seen in Table III.

TABLE III.—*The Effect of the " Loose " Face in Sliced Laminæ 0.10 Inches Thick on the Limiting Radii of Curvature*

Species	Average moisture content (Per cent)	Position of " loose " face in bend	Radius in inches at which losses due to breakages did not exceed 5 per cent of the pieces bent	Approximate ratio : radius/ thickness of laminæ
Sitka Spruce (*Picea sitchensis*)	14.0	Tension side	9.3	93
		Compression side	6.5	65
Western Hemlock (*Tsuga heterophylla*)	13.3	Tension side	7.4	74
		Compression side	5.3	53
Douglas Fir (*Pseudotsuga taxifolia*)	13.2	Tension side	9.0	90
		Compression side	8.5	85

Unfortunately, the ratio of radius/thickness does not appear to be a constant over a wide thickness range, and unless, therefore, an ample safety margin is allowed, it will usually be necessary to carry out a few preliminary tests before deciding upon the most suitable thickness of laminæ to use.

As in the case of thicker solid timber, the bending properties of thin laminæ may be improved, and hence the limiting radii of curvature reduced, by (*a*) increasing the moisture content and (*b*) increasing the temperature of the wood. Advantage is taken of this fact in the method of pre-bending to be described later.

Glues

Almost any type of glue may be used and, in making a choice, such factors as cost, speed of setting, moisture-resisting properties, etc., must of necessity receive due consideration. For furniture work, animal or casein glues might be found quite satisfactory, but where it is essential that the glue should be moisture-resistant as, for example, in the case of aircraft constructional work, a urea-formaldehyde or phenolic type of glue is required. For preference, a glue having gap-filling properties should be used. The gluing technique to be adopted for the production of laminated bends is in all essentials the same as that for flat material and, since detailed information on the procedure to be adopted in using any particular make of glue can usually be obtained from the makers, it is not proposed to deal here with the subject in any great detail. It will suffice to say that in gluing it is essential always to apply uniform and adequate pressure to the glued surfaces until such time as the glue is set, in order to obtain satisfactory bonding of the laminæ.

Pre-bending

In certain instances, where a bend of comparatively small radius of curvature is required, it may prove uneconomical or inconvenient to use laminæ so thin that they may be bent in the cold, dry state without fracture. In such cases, it becomes necessary to improve the bending properties of the wood so far as is possible by the application of heat and moisture and to bend the laminæ roughly to shape. The most convenient way of softening the wood is by immersing the laminæ in boiling water for a period long enough to heat the wood right through to the centre. In this way the limiting radius of all woods, including softwoods, may be considerably reduced as is indicated in Table IV.

TABLE IV.—*The Effect of Immersion in Boiling Water on the Limiting Radius of Curvature of Laminæ $\frac{1}{8}$ Inch Thick*

Species	Treatment	Radius in inches at which losses due to breakages did not exceed 5 per cent of the pieces bent	Approximate ratio : radius/thickness of laminae
Elm, Dutch (home-grown) (*Ulmus hollandica* var. *major*)	None. Immersed in boiling water for 30 minutes.	3.9 1.0	31 8
Beech (home-grown) (*Fagus sylvatica*)	None. Immersed in boiling water for 30 minutes.	4.4 1.6	35 13
Oak (home-grown) (*Quercus robur*)	None. Immersed in boiling water for 30 minutes.	5.8 1.5	46 12
Spruce, Sitka (*Picea sitchensis*)	None. Immersed in boiling water for 30 minutes.	6.0 3.4	48 27

Unfortunately, glue cannot be made to adhere satisfactorily to wood surfaces at much over 20 per cent moisture content, and laminæ so treated will need to be set under restraint and re-dried. Glue is then spread on each of the pre-formed laminæ and the final assembling and pressing carried out in a manner described in Chapter VII.

CHAPTER VII

PRESSING LAMINÆ TO SHAPE

Male and Female Forms

ONE very common method of bending laminated assemblies to shape and of applying the requisite pressure for the proper bonding together of the laminæ is to press them between shaped male and female forms as in Fig. 25.

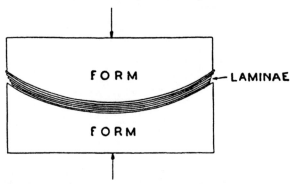

FIG. 25—*A method of pressing laminæ to shape by means of male and female forms*

The pressure may be applied by screws or clamps and must be sufficiently great to conform with the gluing specification laid down by the makers of the particular glue used, making due allowance for the extra pressure required for the actual bending of the material.

Air clamps or hydraulic presses may be employed, and in the case of the latter it is usually found convenient and economical to prepare a series of forms or cauls so as to press a number of assemblies simultaneously. Pressure imposed may then be maintained by means of screw clamps and the whole pack, thus tightly held and secured, removed complete for setting so as to free the press for further work. See Fig. 26.

Forms are usually made of wood and should be well covered with an anti-adhesive paint or coating, but in certain cases metal forms are used.

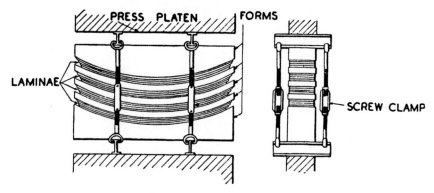

FIG. 26—*Simultaneous pressing of a number of bent members*

Obviously, the male and female forms must be cut accurately to shape if pressure variations from point to point along the length are to be kept at a minimum.

An alternative to the female form is a metal band provided with tightening screws for exerting pressure in the manner illustrated in Fig. 27.

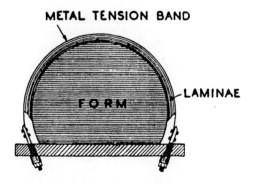

Fig. 27—*A method of pressing laminæ to shape by means of a metal tension band*

Both these methods, however, are open to the objection that greater pressure must of necessity be exerted at the vertex of the bend than at the ends. This objection can, to a certain extent, be overcome by splitting the male or female forms into a number of segments and clamping each independently as in Fig. 28, or by applying radial pressure at a number of points to a flexible band acting in place of the female form. Such an arrangement is shown in Fig. 29, where the band consists of a number of thin wooden strips pre-bent roughly to the shape required. Radial pressure here is applied by means of wedges, though other suitable clamping devices might be used.

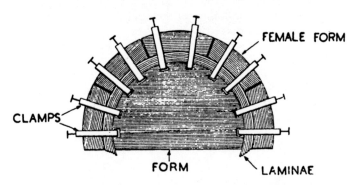

Fig. 28—*A method of pressing laminæ to shape by means of split female forms*

Fluid Pressure

The best method of applying uniform pressure over the complete surface area of a bend is by means of fluid pressure. One way of doing this is to incorporate a flexible rubber hose or tube between one form and the laminated assembly. After bending the glued laminæ and securing the forms in the required relative positions, the tube is inflated by means of air or water until

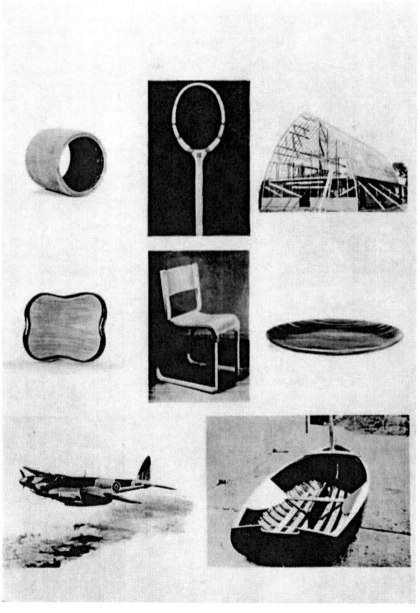

Laminated glued arches—Courtesy of Editor of the journal " Wood ".
Laminated chair   — ,,   ,, *The Educational Supply Association, Ltd.*
Sailing dinghy   — ,,   ,, *Aero Research, Ltd.*
Aeroplane   — ,.   ,, *the De Havilland Aircraft Co., Ltd.*

PLATE 17—Examples of laminated bends as used in industry

PLATE 18—Air-inflated tubular hose and low voltage strip-heating used in the production of laminated bends

By courtesy of *William Lawrence & Co., Ltd.*

PLATE 19—Pressure moulding bag

PLATE 20—Laminated bending by the autoclave process (rubber bag removed)

the desired pressure is read on the gauge (see Fig. 30 and Plate 18). By this means pressure is applied radially and uniformly along the complete length of bend and only one form need be cut accurately to shape. Usually, though not always, it is the male form that is employed as a mould, since the bending operation is performed more easily around a convex mould than inside a concave one. In certain instances, however, an expanding rubber hose or bag

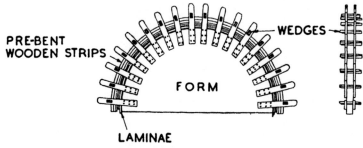

FIG. 29—*A method of pressing laminæ to shape by means of pre-bent wooden strips and wedges*

may take the place of the male form, in which case the laminated assembly is first roughly bent by hand to the shape of the female form and then pressed tightly to exact shape by fluid pressure (see Fig. 31).

In like manner a rubber sheet or bag may take the place of the female form and Fig. 32 shows a set-up in which the laminæ and mould are placed inside a rubber bag and bent and pressed to shape by exhausting the bag of air so as to subject the wood to atmospheric pressure of about 14 lb./sq. inch. For the

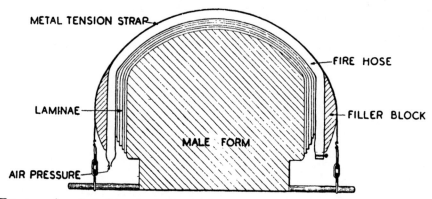

FIG. 30—*A method of pressing laminæ to shape by means of an inflated flexible rubber hose and a metal strap*

proper bending and bonding of thick laminæ such a pressure is often found to be insufficient, in which case it may be augmented by placing the bag, mould and laminated assembly in an autoclave or pressure cylinder, as shown in Plates 19 and 20. Here, as before, trapped air is exhausted or allowed to escape from under the rubber, and air at pressures higher than atmospheric is applied to the top side so that virtually any desired pressure may thus be applied normal to the surface of the bent part.

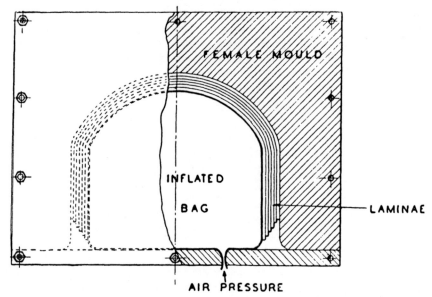

FIG. 31—*A method of pressing laminæ to shape by means of an inflated rubber bag and female mould*

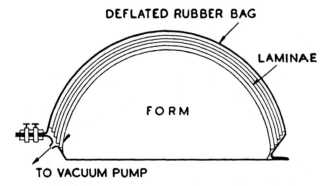

FIG. 32—*A method of pressing laminæ to shape by means of a deflated rubber bag*

The Continuous Strip Method

Continuous type bends such as may be used for chair seat rings cannot readily be made by any of the methods so far described and, in consequence, are often fabricated by scarfing together two or more curved segments to form the completed whole. This latter method obviously has the disadvantage of introducing possible planes of weakness across the section at the scarf joints, as well as the trouble of making such joints in the assembly. An improved method, which has been developed recently at the Forest Products Research Laboratory, of making continuous type bends that are not subject to the above disadvantages consists of scarfing end to end lengths of laminæ to form a continuous strip, which is then wound around the form under pressure as described below.

Laminæ of the required width of bend are prepared at a moisture content of about 15 per cent, and these are provided with scarfs at each end. It is essential that the scarfs should be smooth and accurately made, and a sanding machine has been found very suitable for this purpose. Any reasonable length of piece may be used from almost any species of timber, and the thickness is limited only by the bending properties of the particular species and radius of bend. The prepared pieces are next glued end to end in one long length by means of scarf joints which, for satisfactory results, should have an inclination of about 1 in 15. It must be emphasized that success in bending will be dependent to a large extent upon the bonding of these scarf joints, and that care should be taken to ensure complete contact of the surfaces to be joined and perfect adhesion. The completed strip is then wrapped loosely around a drum or spider from which it may readily be fed on to the bending form. The form may be of wood or metal with a profile of the required shape and fitted with a shelf at the top to act as a guide when the wood is fed on to it (see Plate 21).

It is also provided with a slot into which fits a wooden block that has been glued to the strip some 2 inches from one end. This form is mounted on a revolving table driven by an electric motor or other mechanical means, and the end of strip attached to it by slipping the block into the slot. When now the table is revolved, the form is caused to rotate and the strip is wrapped around it in spiral form. After a complete turn has been wrapped on the form glue is applied to one face of the strip, usually by means of a glue spreader situated at some suitable point along the straight length of strip as it feeds on to the form (see Plate 22).

The success of the gluing operation is now dependent, as always, not only on the efficiency of the glue and glue-spreading, but also on the proper regulation of the pressure applied across the surfaces.

The method of applying pressure in continuous strip bending is by means of a tensioned belt which throughout the bending operation embraces the wood and form in the manner of a band-brake (see Plate 21).

" Balata " type belting has been found suitable for this work and, in the set-up shown, one end of a length of belting is anchored securely and the belt itself, after being passed around the form and the back of the bent strip, is subjected to a tensile stress at the other end. Tension may be applied by a suitable system of weights and levers, or by means of a spring-loaded motor-driven tensioning device such as has been recently installed at the Laboratory. For mass-producing one particular type of bend, the simplest method is probably that shown in Plate 21, where the load is applied by suspending a box of weights from a rope attached to the end of the belt. If such a system is used it will be necessary to incorporate some form of mechanical lifting device to support the load and slacken the belt after the completion of a bend to avoid repeatedly having to load and unload the box of weights. The exact load required will depend upon several factors, such as species and thickness of laminæ, radius of curvature, etc., and can best be determined from experience. As a rough guide, however, a minimum load of 200 lb. per inch width of bend is suggested. A clamp must always be fitted to hold the wood in place before the final release of pressure in the belt. A large variety of continuous-shape types of bend may be made by this method and obviously many non-continuous types may be obtained from these by cross-cutting if desired. A selection of

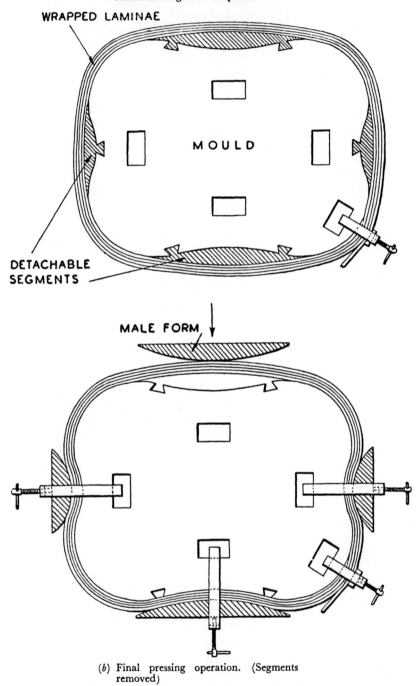

(a) Wooden strip wound on to mould with detachable segments in position

WRAPPED LAMINAE

MOULD

DETACHABLE SEGMENTS

MALE FORM

(b) Final pressing operation. (Segments removed)

FIG. 33—*A method of making re-entrant laminated bends by the Forest Products Research Laboratory continuous strip process*

bends so made is shown in Plate 23, and it will be noted that it has been found possible to produce shapes which include re-entrant curves. The method adopted for making re-entrant bends has been to fit detachable segments to the form in the manner shown in Fig. 33. With these in position during the initial bending operation, it is clear that what subsequently will be the re-entrant portions are first bent in exactly the opposite sense so as to bulge outwards. By this means the extra length of material required for the re-entrants is secured. It is later possible, before the glue has set, to remove the detachable segments and by means of clamps and male forms to force inwards such parts of the bend as were in contact with these segments, so as to conform to the re-entrant curves desired (see Fig. 33). There is, of course, a limit to the variety of shapes that can thus be produced, and it is necessary to stress that by this method it is impossible to ensure good contact of the wood along straight portions of a form. For this reason, all straight portions of appreciable length, along which the wood has a natural tendency to belly outwards, should be held flat during setting by means of boards and clamps. A further machine of this type, as used in commerce, is shown in Plate 22.

Laminated Inserts

The insert method of producing bent parts is often adopted when the finished wooden member is to be for the most part straight, but is to contain a curved portion at one or both ends.

The method consists in making longitudinal saw cuts along the length of the part to be bent, so spaced that the thickness of the tongues left between the slots are not likely to fracture in the bending operation. Glue-covered laminæ cut to the exact length and thickness of the slots are then inserted, and the bend made under pressure around a form in a manner such as has already been described for the bending of laminated assemblies (see Fig. 34). It is, of course, necessary to ensure that the thickness of the inserts and of the tongues is such as to permit the bend to be made without undue difficulty or fracturing. In order to avoid excessive weakening of the sections, the slots should be of varying length so that the ends of the inserts will not be along one cross-section.

Two-plane Bends

The bending of laminæ in the one plane usually presents little difficulty, but the same cannot be said for bending in two planes, and some such method as the following will need to be employed. Laminæ, glued and assembled in the normal manner, are first bent in one plane to the radius of curvature required. This bend might, for instance, take the form of a U having straight legs of sufficient length to provide material for those portions later to be bent in a plane at right angles to the first. The initial bend, after setting, is then sawn parallel to the thickness into a number of thin curved laminæ and glue spread on the surfaces. These are then assembled on the two-plane form, and pressure applied to re-unite the central curved portion and to bend and clamp the legs in position. In applying this method, it is obviously necessary to allow, in the initial width of bend, for the wood that is to be removed by the saw cuts, and in this respect the method is somewhat wasteful of material. Some appreciable saving of material might be effected by slotting the legs of the initial bend and employing the insert method, described above, for the bend in the other plane.

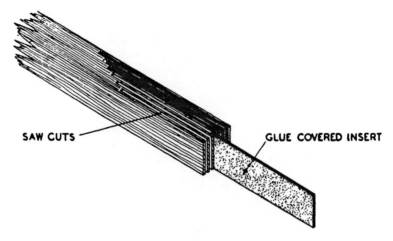

SAW CUTS

GLUE COVERED INSERT

FIG. 34A—*A laminated bend made by the insert method. Assembly of glue-covered inserts*

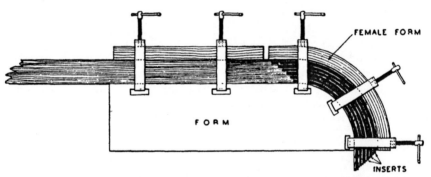

FEMALE FORM

FORM

INSERTS

FIG. 34B—*A laminated bend made by the insert method. Bending and pressing*

Laminated Tubes and Cylinders

The continuous strip method is one that obviously lends itself to the production of laminated cylinders, and examples of cylinders or drums so produced are shown in Plate 24. Another method that has been adopted for the manufacture of masts and spars for ships consists essentially of bending across the grain a series of tubes which fit one over the other to give the required wall thickness, Sitka spruce being the species usually employed. The methods of softening and bending the individual layers have been described previously under the heading " Pre-bending ".

In the final operation, each concentric tube is scarf-jointed and bonded to the next by the application of glue and radial pressure. In Plate 25 completed laminated tubes or cylinders so formed are illustrated.

A third method consists of placing a number of pre-formed laminæ, or thin sheets of plywood, inside a metal tube in such a manner that they form concentric and curved layers fitting reasonably close to the walls of the metal tube. Just prior to assembling, glue is spread over the surfaces of each layer and, once assembled within the tube, a cylindrically-shaped rubber bag is introduced into the space remaining along the axis of the tube. The top and bottom of the tube are tightly sealed and fluid pressure is introduced into the rubber bag, which causes pressure to be exerted radially against the layers of wood. By such means, the concentric layers are pressed tightly one against the other and, once the glue is set, the laminated cylinder is complete. Individual laminæ or sheets may be jointed by means of scarf, butt, or lap joints according to the final appearance and finish required. An expanding metal or wooden form may sometimes be substituted for the rubber bag and a tightened steel band for the metal tube.

Finally, mention may be made of the method described in British Patent Specification No. 550,400 whereby strips of wood sheeting, veneer or the like are wound helically around a heated metal tube.

Moulding

Unlike certain metals, wood is fissile, and hence not very malleable, so that it cannot easily be moulded or bent in the one operation in two directions at right angles to one another. Some comparatively simple shapes containing compound curvature can indeed be made by pressing veneer sheets between male and female moulds, but if, for instance, it were required that a thin sheet be made to conform to the surface contours of a portion of a sphere of relatively small radius, creases or folds would tend to appear in much the same way as when a sheet of paper is wrapped tightly around an orange. In the development of these folds the structural upsets would soon reach a value sufficient to fracture the wood.

To overcome this difficulty and to make possible the production of complex shapes, it is usual to employ veneers which have been " tailored " or cut so that on applying the pressure necessary to make the wood conform to the shape of the mould, the edges of the cuts come close to one another and form tightly fitting joints or seams.

Tailoring, as the name would imply, consists essentially, therefore, in fashioning or cutting the veneers to fit the mould in much the same way as a tailor would cut cloth for a garment, realizing that when the pieces have been fitted together and the seams stitched the garment must fit accurately to shape.

In building up consecutive layers of veneers on a mould, one of two methods is normally used.

In the first method, the " tailored " sheets, which may take the form of tapered strips or of pieces from which nicks or slots have been cut, are assembled one at a time on a mould of wooden construction. These are held in place by means of tacks or clips and, if cut correctly, the material will fit snugly to shape with butt joints appearing in place of what otherwise would be creases or fractures. When one complete layer has been applied to the mould in this way, glue is spread over the exposed surface and the next layer is fitted in a similar manner. As each successive layer is applied, the tacks in the preceding one are removed. Those remaining in the outer layer are finally removed after the adhesive has been cured or set.

In the second method of making complex shapes, a pre-forming process is used in which the veneer sheet or sheets comprising one layer are tailored and bent roughly to the required shape and edge-jointed before actual assembly on the mould. The veneers are often pre-formed by moistening and pressing between male and female dies. The butt joints or seams are usually " soldered " together by the application of animal glue, formaldehyde and a hot iron. Strips and pieces forming the outer layer are usually edge-jointed by means of adhesive tape.

By feathering the edges, scarf joints may be formed instead of butt joints and the layers are often made of two-ply instead of the single veneer.

When the requisite number of sheets or layers have been pre-formed in the above manner the surfaces are covered with glue and placed one on top of the other over a male form or mould. Fluid pressure may then be applied to the assembly by means of a rubber sheet or bag (Plates 19 and 20). When film glue is used, requiring high temperatures and pressures, steam-heated metal male and female moulds are commonly employed.

CHAPTER VIII

GLUE SETTING

The Setting of Laminated Bends

THE setting to shape of laminated bends is essentially a process of glue setting, and the method used will, therefore, depend to a large extent on the type of glue used. Other factors, such as, for instance, the rate of production required, cost, etc., will, however, need to be considered before any particular method of setting is decided upon. In general, any method which is employed for setting glues in the manufacture of laminated flat assemblies can also be used in bent work. It should, however, be noted that on release of external pressure the glue layers in bent members are stressed considerably more than in flat assemblies and for this reason slightly longer pressing periods are normally required.

Most of the older glues, such as, for example, those of the animal or vegetable types, are applied hot, and in most cases it is essential to ensure that such glue has cooled completely before the bend can be removed from the jig without fear of delamination or glue failure. Normally, with glues of this type, the bends remain clamped or pressed to shape overnight, but with certain special mixes it is sometimes possible to remove them after a period of about 3 to 4 hours. Setting periods may sometimes be reduced if warm air is circulated around the jig, thereby increasing the rate of setting of the edges of the glue layers.

Unlike the glues of the animal and vegetable types, the caseins and synthetic resins become set by virtue of chemical changes taking place in the adhesive, as well as by the loss of moisture, both of which effects can be accelerated by increased temperatures. By the quick setting of these glues at high temperatures, not only can the rate of production be increased, but the number of bending jigs required can be kept to a minimum.

Heat can be applied to the laminated component in a variety of ways, such as by removing the assembly to a heated room, heating the jig by means of steam, hot water or electricity, etc. Another method is to incorporate in the system electrically heated blankets or low voltage heating strips.

Strip Heating

The strip heating process, which was developed for use in the mass production of laminated bends for wooden aircraft during the second world war, has proved to be one of the most convenient methods of applying heat to glue layers.

The heating elements usually consist of steel strips carrying a low tension current of high amperage. Fig. 35 and Plate 18 show how a bend on conventional jigs may be heated by this method, using steel strips in close contact

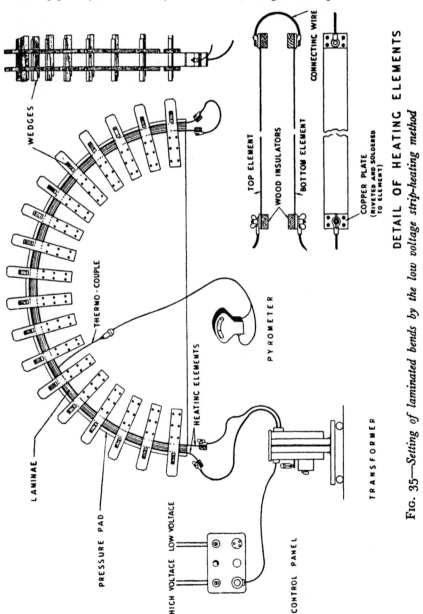

FIG. 35—Setting of laminated bends by the low voltage strip-heating method

with the faces. The strips are joined together at one end and at the other are connected to a step-down transformer. The resistance which the strips offer to a current passing through them causes heat to be generated which is conducted through the wood laminæ to the glue layers. Temperature control is usually obtained by regulating the current flowing through the strips, either by altering the voltage on the output side of the transformer or by increasing the lengths of the freely exposed ends of the strips, which should, of course, be insulated one from the other.

The electrical energy necessary to produce the desired temperature in the strip heater will depend on several variables, such as size, shape and construction of jigs, but a power consumption of about 1.75 watts per square inch of strip surface area, or approximately ¼ kilowatt per square foot, has been found to be generally satisfactory.

Thus, if the total area of the metal strips is 4 square feet, a transformer of at least 1 kilowatt will be required, and it is recommended for the safety of the operators that the voltage on the output side should not exceed 12 volts.

In order to get the load matched with the transformer it is necessary to determine first the minimum load resistance for the transformer and then to calculate the thickness or gauge of the strip which can safely be used. If " K " is the power output in kilowatts and " E " is the output voltage, then the minimum load resistance " R " for the transformer is given by

$$R = \frac{E^2}{1000 \ K}$$

Thus, for a ½ kilowatt transformer with an output voltage of 4¼ volts, the minimum load resistance would be 0.036 ohms.

In designing the heating strips, it is usual to arrange for these to be of sufficient length and width so as completely to cover the surfaces to be heated. Furthermore, although in Fig. 35 these are shown as loose strips connected in series, it is sometimes more convenient to arrange for the strips to be attached to the jig and connected in parallel.

Finally, it is necessary to calculate the thickness or gauge of the strips so as to get the load matched with the transformer. The calculation follows from the electrical relationship, namely :—

$$\text{Electrical Resistance} = \frac{\text{Specific resistance} \times \text{Length}}{\text{Area of cross-section}}$$

$$\text{or } R = \frac{S \times L}{A} = \frac{S \times L}{B \times T} \text{ where}$$

S = Specific Resistance.
L = Length.
B = Breadth.
T = Thickness.
A = Area of cross-section.

Assume, for example, that it is required to determine the thickness T of a steel strip which is 14 ft. (168 in.) long and 2 in. wide for use with a transformer with a minimum load resistance of 0.036 ohms, and the specific resistance of the steel is given as 20×10^{-6} in ohm centimetre units, then by substituting these values in the equation above we get :

$$0.036 = \frac{20 \times 10^{-6} \times 168}{2 \times T \times 2.54}$$

$$\text{or } T = \frac{20 \times 10^{-6} \times 168}{0.036 \times 2 \times 2.54} = 0.0183 \text{ in. or 26 S.W.G.}$$

Determination of Setting Times

When the transference of heat through a glued assembly is by means of conduction, the curing of the glue in any layer is not taking place at any one fixed temperature.

The setting or curing time of a resin glue at any given temperature may differ appreciably from that of another, and in order to determine minimum setting times required for a glued assembly, temperature measurements need to be taken and used in conjunction with the glue manufacturer's stated curing times at the various temperatures.

When comparatively low temperatures are employed temperature measurements may be made by means of the ordinary mercury in glass thermometers, but when strip heating or similar methods of accelerated setting are employed they are best made by means of thermocouples.

In estimating the minimum setting times by the thermocouple method it is necessary to insert a thermocouple in the glue line of a sample bend as remote from the source of heat as possible, since the time of setting there will be longer than at any of the other glue lines.

Since in the case of certain glues, such as, for example, cold-setting synthetic resins of the urea-formaldehyde type, glue line failures are induced when the temperature anywhere exceeds boiling point, *i.e.* $212°$ F., it is advisable to introduce an additional thermocouple to measure the temperature at the hottest spot, namely, between the heating element and the surface of the glued assembly.

When temperature measurements have been made, setting times can then most simply be computed by adding together the time taken for the remote glue layer to reach a particular temperature and the time required for the glue to cure at this temperature. Setting periods so estimated will vary according to the temperature value selected, and it is advisable to make two or three such estimates to ensure that the period finally chosen is not unnecessarily prolonged.

In this method of computing the setting time, no allowance has been made for the fact that setting takes place as the temperature of the glue gradually increases. A second method of computing setting times to allow for this temperature increase has been developed at the Laboratory.* In this method a smooth curve is first plotted of the rate of rise in temperature, and this is later replaced by a stepped curve (see Fig. 36) obtained as follows : The temperature is imagined to remain constant for a minute and then to rise suddenly to the average value of the smooth curve during the next minute. The rate of curing of an adhesive, at $180°$ F. is, say, eight minutes, and it may be assumed that the reaction of setting has proceeded one-eighth of the way to completion during one minute at this temperature (this assumption cannot be taken as

---

* A. R. BRYANT. *The Bonding of Tego Film Glue in Plywood.* British Tego Glue Film, Ltd., London, 1941. 16 pp.

fully proved, but is justified by results in practice). Under each of the one-minute intervals of the stepped curve in Fig. 36 is written the fraction of the total polymerization or cure which may thus be supposed to have taken place during that particular minute. These fractions are then added up, and when their total reaches unity the reaction is then considered complete and the glue fully cured. In the particular example in Fig. 36 the sum of the fractions reaches unity at the end of 29 minutes.

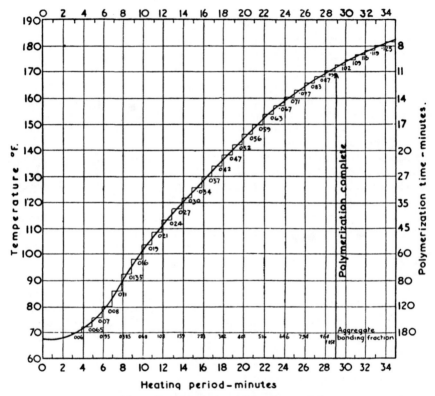

FIG. 36—*Calculation of heating period*

Bends set in this way may be removed hot, but if this is done the jigs must be cooled before re-filling, if reproducible results are to be obtained.

By some it is considered better practice partly to cool the bend while on the jig, in which case this period might be taken into consideration in determining minimum setting times.

Miscellaneous Setting Methods

During recent years, other methods of heating glue layers have been developed, but these are either still in the experimental stage or have proved to be somewhat costly. Examples of these are heating by infra-red rays, by radio frequency power, or by the passage of an electric current through a wire or gauze embedded in the glue layer.

Probably the most promising of these relatively new methods of accelerating the setting of glues is the electrostatic process in which the glued laminæ are placed in an electric field which oscillates at high frequencies and results in heating occurring uniformly throughout the mass.

This method appears to be especially well adapted to the gluing of thick laminated members, such as laminated roof trusses, stems for boats, etc., where other methods are time-consuming or impractical. The process, however, is still in the developmental stage, and much work remains to be done.

CHAPTER IX

THE MOVEMENT AND DISTORTION OF LAMINATED BENDS

The Movement of Laminated Bends

EACH lamina in a bent assembly has an inherent tendency to return to its original shape and, but for the bonding of the glue, a bend would straighten out as soon as the externally applied forces were removed. On removing a laminated bend from a form, outward movement does, in fact, tend to occur and shear stresses are induced in the glue lines. Movement continues until the induced moment of resistance in the piece just balances the residual bending moments in the laminæ. Shear forces in the glue tend to be greater near the ends than at the centre of a bend, and movement or straightening is, therefore, always more pronounced near the ends.*

The extent of this outward movement is usually small when a number of comparatively thin laminæ are used, and the effect is often masked by such movements as are consequent upon change of moisture.

Other things being equal, the thinner the laminæ the less the tendency for a " set " bend to open on release of the pressure but, unfortunately, the thinner the laminæ the greater the quantity of glue used.

All glues normally used for bent work contain moisture in varying amounts, which naturally tends to find its way into the wood and so raise its moisture content. Since setting usually occurs before all this moisture is removed, the bend tends subsequently to dry out in the workshop or in service, with consequent reduction in the radius of curvature.

Ideally, therefore, the amount of moisture added by the glue, and the consequent inward movement caused by its removal, should be just enough to compensate for the initial outward movement referred to above.

In actual practice, however, control of this process is virtually impossible, and where accuracy of shape is of paramount importance it is advisable to use a glue containing as little moisture as possible. The minimum quantity consistent with strength should be used, and the laminæ conditioned initially to a moisture content corresponding to conditions of service. Solely from this aspect, glue types may be graded as follows :—

> Phenol-formaldehyde,
> Urea-formaldehyde,
> Casein, and
> Animal.

---

* W. W. BARKAS. *Tangential and Radial Stresses in Two-ply Circular Bends.* Forest Products Research Laboratory, Unpublished Report, August 1945.

Naturally, in the selection of any glue for a specific purpose, other aspects such as strength, resistance to moisture, cost, etc., need to be taken into consideration. The general principles involved in the movement of bends consequent upon moisture change are dealt with more fully in the next chapter.

Distortion of Bends

In the bending of any elastic material, compression and tensile stresses are induced along the concave and convex surfaces respectively. These direct stresses tend always to produce strains in their own direction, but at the same time to produce opposite kinds of strain in perpendicular directions. Thus the longitudinal shortening of the compressed concave surface is accompanied by a lateral expansion, and similarly the longitudinal stretch of the convex surface is accompanied by a lateral shortening. It thus follows that by bending the material in one plane a tendency will be induced for it to bend in a plane at right angles to the first but in the opposite sense.

Such curvature as may result from bending moments so induced appears in the form of " cupping " of the cross-section of a bent piece, but usually the extent of the distortion so produced is small and of little consequence.

Curved or flat laminated assemblies containing grain that deviates from the straight are, however, subject to distortion as the result of *moisture change* in much the same way as boards of solid timber. If wood with curved grain is used there will be a tendency, when drying occurs, for the piece as a whole to curve

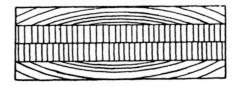

Fig. 37—*End view of laminated assembly with annual rings so arranged as to counteract cupping tendency*

in the same direction as the curvature of the grain. Similarly, if the grain is in spiral form there will be a tendency for the assembly on drying to twist. Troubles from such causes obviously can be eliminated by selecting only straight-grained material for the work and, above all, by ensuring that all pieces are conditioned to one and the same moisture content before assembly.

Even with the use of straight-grained material, however, curvature of the cross-section, usually referred to as " cupping ", may occur unless the material is properly quartered. Flat-sawn laminæ assembled so that the annual rings, as they appear on the ends, are more or less concentric, will curve or " cup " on drying in a direction opposite to that of the ring curvature.

Still more marked would be the effect if the top half of an assembly consisted of flat-sawn material and the bottom half of quarter-sawn, since stresses would be set up across the section and glue lines as a result of excess shrinkage or expansion of the slash over the quartered material, leading to curvature of the section. It is possible to minimize such effects by assembling individual laminæ in some such balanced manner as that shown in Fig. 37, so that the tendency of any pair to curve in one direction is offset by a like tendency for another pair to curve in the other direction. As, however, stresses in the glue lines are thereby induced this method cannot generally be recommended.

Moreover, it must be realized that, in applying such methods, the balance of stress so achieved may be upset by subsequent machining of the parts.

Straightness of grain does not preclude the possibility of the laminated assembly twisting as a result of moisture change unless the grain is absolutely parallel with the sides, or parallel grain exists throughout the assembly. To illustrate the effect that inclination of grain may have upon the twisting of laminated bends, Fig. 38 is drawn to represent an assembly made of two laminæ with the grain of the top piece inclined at an angle to the grain of the bottom. The diagonal lines are meant to represent grain lines as they appeared before assembly on the top and bottom pieces. The inclination of the grain to the sides of each lamina is assumed here to be the same.

If now it is assumed that virtually no shrinkage takes place in the direction of the grain but that there is shrinkage in the direction normal to the grain as a result of drying, it is apparent that the top right-hand corner X and bottom left-hand corner Y of the top lamina will tend to approach one another, and the other two corners will also tend to approach one another, but to a much less extent. The face of the lamina will in effect diamond, and the longer edges tend to orientate themselves in the direction of the grain. The lower lamina will behave similarly, but the orientation will be in the opposite direction.

If free to move then, the end sections would assume relative positions as illustrated diagrammatically in Fig. 38. The glue, however, inhibits

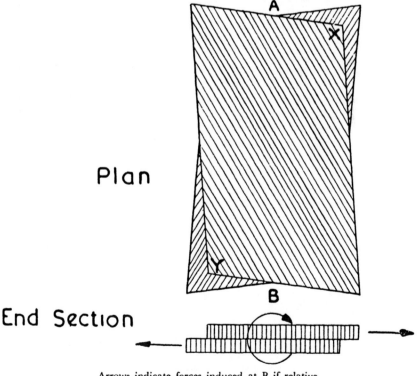

Arrows indicate forces induced at B if relative movement of laminæ is inhibited by gluing

FIG. 38—*Diamonding effect leading to twist*

the relative movement, and consequently forces are developed, with the top lamina pulling in one direction with a force P, and the bottom in the other direction with an equal force P. These two forces form a couple or turning moment which tends to twist one end in an anti-clockwise direction and the other in a clockwise direction as viewed from either end. The whole piece is thus subjected to torsion, and twisting is the probable outcome.

From the above it follows that by crossing the grain of two or more laminæ in a pack, a tendency for the glued assembly to twist is induced as a result of subsequent moisture change. The intensity of twisting likely to develop will be dependent upon a number of factors, such as degree of moisture change, the angle of crossing of the grain lines, the relative positions and thicknesses of the parts having opposed grain, strength characteristics, etc.

It has been suggested that twist may be minimized by assembling the laminæ so that the annual rings on the end cross-section form a " herringbone " pattern (see Fig. 39). Tests have shown, however, that this method of assembly has

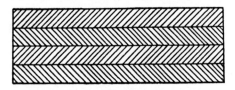

FIG. 39—*End view of laminated assembly with annual rings arranged in herringbone pattern*

little if any control upon subsequent twisting, which fact is illustrated by the bends shown in Plate 26. Here the bend marked " A " was made from an assembly of laminæ having grain at an angle to the sides but parallel throughout and with the annual rings on the end section sloping in one direction. The bend marked " B " was made from matched material, but assembled so that the grain of the lamina on the concave face was sloping in the opposite direction to the remainder. The annual rings on the end section of this particular bend were in perfect " herringbone " formation, yet, as may be observed, the twist that subsequently developed was very pronounced.

The herringbone assembly method hence can be recommended only in so far as it tends to minimize subsequent " cupping " of the cross-section of a piece.

The best method of avoiding twisting troubles would seem to be that of selecting perfectly straight-grained material having the grain absolutely parallel with the length of piece. Failing this, however, it is recommended that the greatest care should be taken to ensure that the grain of the several laminæ in a pack is parallel throughout, which requirement can best be fulfilled by assembling the packs from laminæ in the order cut. Twisting may also, of course, be minimized or eliminated by arranging that any pair of laminæ with crossed grain, which would tend to twist the assembled bend, say, to the right, is counterbalanced by another pair tending to twist it with an equal force to the left. Such balancing is not easy to accomplish in practice and is not to be recommended as a general method of procedure. Finally, if none of the above methods proves feasible, it remains to ensure so far as possible that the moisture content of the bent pieces does not alter after setting, so that no shrinkage or

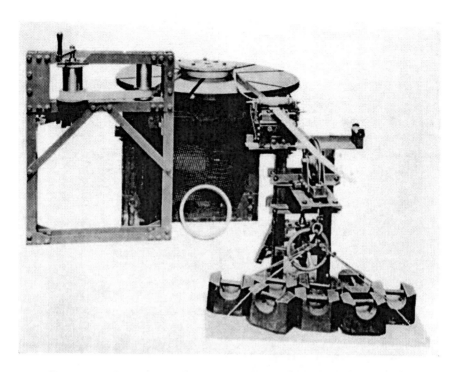

PLATE 21—Laminated bending by the continuous strip method

PLATE 22—A commercial machine employed for the production of
laminated bends by the continuous strip method

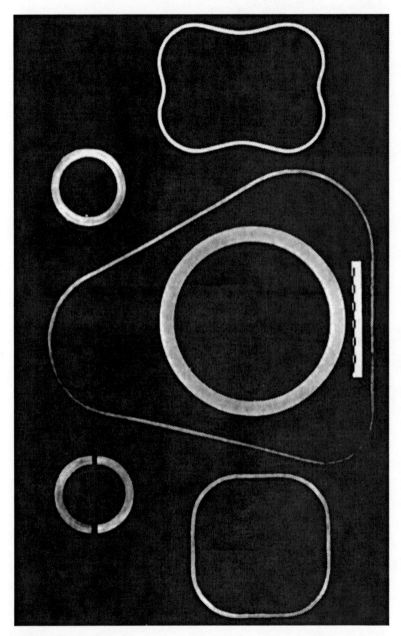

PLATE 23—A selection of laminated bends made by the F.P.R.L. strip-winding process

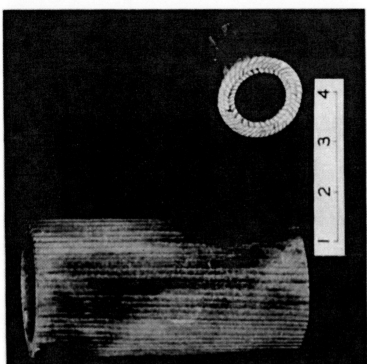

PLATE 25—Sections of hollow spars made of Sitka spruce laminæ bent across the grain

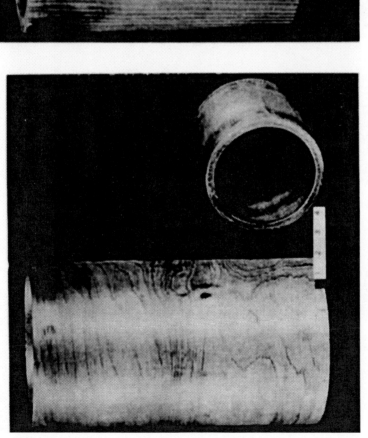

PLATE 24—Laminated cylinders made by the continuous strip method

PLATE 26—The twisting of laminated bends

Bend " A ".—Assembled with the grain of all laminæ parallel and annual rings on end-section sloping in one direction.

Bend " B ".—Assembled with the grain of one lamina on concave face sloping in the opposite direction to remainder and with annual rings forming " herringbone " pattern on end-section.

swelling occurs up to the time that they are incorporated in the finished product. Bends already twisted may, of course, be similarly made serviceable by conditioning back to their original moisture value, but it must be borne in mind that when subsequent moisture changes occur in service, such conditioned bends may cause trouble by twisting out of shape and possibly producing distortions in the finished article in which they are incorporated.

CHAPTER X

THEORETICAL CONSIDERATIONS

Assessment of Bending Qualities from Compressive and Tensile Stress-strain Relationships

SINCE the process of bending consists essentially of compressing some and stretching other fibres of a piece of wood, it should be possible to determine theoretically its bending properties, and the bending forces involved, from a knowledge of the simple stress-strain relationships of wood.

Such a method of determination involving the testing of small specimens in standard type testing machines would have obvious advantages over the direct method of testing comparatively large specimens on a specially designed bending machine. Moreover, it should also prove useful in the determination not only of the limiting radii of curvature, in bending both with and without a strap, but also of the bending moments and end-pressures set up in making a bend of any given radius and thickness. Consequently, a considerable number of experiments were carried out at the Forest Products Research Laboratory to ascertain whether, in fact, straightforward compression and tension tests could be made to yield reliable data relating to the bending properties of steamed wood, the problem being approached on the lines suggested by A. Prodehl in his treatise on the bending of steamed wood.*

Fig. 40 has been drawn to represent a bending machine such as the one built for standard bending tests at the Laboratory, resembling somewhat the

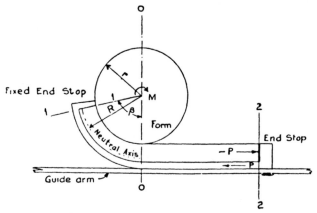

FIG. 40—*Diagrammatic representation of a bending machine*

* *Untersuchungen uber das Biegen gedämpften Holzes.* Rotaprint von der Sächsischen Technischen Hochschule, Dresden.

commercial machine for making seat rings, which is shown in Plate 12.   In this type of machine the form is caused to revolve and wrap the wood around itself, but the general principles and theoretical considerations involved in the bending process are the same as in the case of a machine in which the wood is wrapped around a stationary form.   A fixed end-stop is clamped to the form, and the other end-stop is fixed to the strap and is capable of moving only in the direction of the guide arm.   The steel strap joining the two end-stops keeps the wood tightly pressed at the ends during the whole bending operation.   The line 1–1 represents the end of the bent portion of the wood ;   the unbent portion lies between the lines 0–0 and 2–2.   The latter is caused by the guide arm to move in a straight line up to the point of contact of the wood and form.

In the calculations given below, the following assumptions were made :—

(1) The originally plane right cross-sections of the wood and strap remain plane during bending

(2) There is free movement between wood and metal strap

(3) The same stress distribution exists between each cross-section of the wood/strap system between the lines 0–0 and 2–2 of the diagram, Fig. 40

(4) The friction between wood and strap and wood and form may be neglected for the simplification of the calculations, and

(5) The thickness and stretch of the strong steel strap are small compared with those of the wood and can be neglected.

In the equations let " b " be the breadth and " 1 " the length of the strap ; " B " the breadth, " S " the thickness, and " L " the original length of the wood ;   " p " the intensity of stress, and " e " the strain in the wood and strap ;   " r " the radius of form and " R " the radius of the neutral axis of the bent wood ; and " β " the bending angle, i.e. the angle subtended by the bent portion on the form.

End Pressures

From the assumptions made, the uniform stress " p " in the still unbent portion of the wood between 0–0 and 2–2 gives a total pressure −P (compressive) such that

$$-P = p.B.S. \quad \ldots \ldots (1)$$

This force is transmitted to the strap, and since friction and the induced strains in the strap caused by bending of the metal may be neglected, the force P exists unchanged along the whole length of the strap.

Consider now a thin layer of wood of thickness dx on the curved portion between 0–0 and 1–1 at a distance $(r+x)$ from the centre of the form. Assuming this thin layer to have been originally of length " y " before bending, we get

$$\frac{r+x}{y\,(1+e_x)} = \frac{R}{y}$$

so $R\,(1+e_x) = r+x \quad \ldots \ldots (2)$

and (differentiating)

$$R\,de_x = dx \quad \ldots \ldots (3)$$

The total pressure −P in the bent portion of the wood is given as :

$$-P = B\Sigma_{x=0}^{x=S} p_x dx$$

Now p is a function of e and is obtainable from the stress/strain curves of the wood in any given condition.   Hence

$$p = f(e) \ . \ . \ . \ . \ . \ . \ (4)$$

And substituting for p and dx we get

$$-P = BR\Sigma \ f(e) \ de \quad \begin{array}{c} e = \left(\dfrac{r+S}{R} - I \right) \\[2ex] e = \left(\dfrac{r}{R} - I \right) \end{array} \quad \ . \ . \ . \ . \ . \ . \ (5)$$

Tension and Compression Tests

Tests for determining the stress/strain relationships of steamed wood both for compression and tension have been carried out at the Laboratory by the Section of Timber Mechanics.   Specimens $1 \times 1 \times 1\frac{3}{4}$ inches were cut and machined to provide material for determining the stress/strain relationships

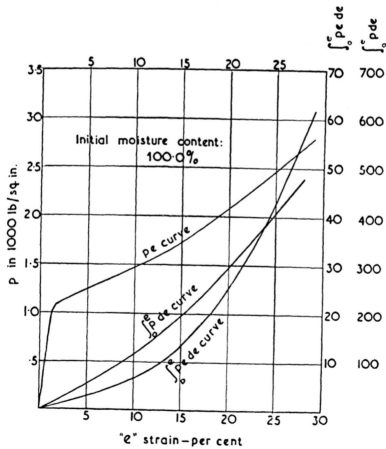

Fig. 41—*Compressive stress/strain curves of steamed home-grown beech*

in compression, and these were compressed parallel to the grain and in the direction of the greatest length.

The stress/strain relationships in tension were determined on specimens $1 \times \frac{1}{4}$ inch in cross-section and 10 inches in length.

All specimens were steamed in a small atmospheric steaming-oven situated close to the testing machine, and care was taken to ensure that the minimum heat loss occurred before the actual test was in progress.

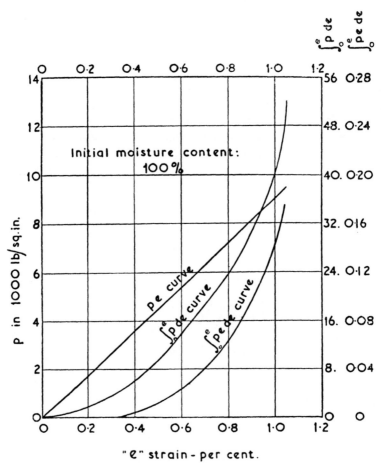

FIG. 42—*Tensile stress/strain curves of steamed home-grown beech*

The rate of straining in compression was 0.15 in. per minute, and in tension 0.25 in. per minute.

The measurement of the tensile strain presented a certain amount of difficulty, and a special form of extensometer and multiplying device was developed for the purpose.

Typical stress-strain relationship curves (p e curves) obtained for English beech, taken to the points where fractures occurred, are shown in Figs. 41 and 42. Area curves are also shown on these graphs, and reference to these will be made later in the calculations.

Minimum Radius

From such curves, an estimate of the minimum bending radius of curvature may be made in the following manner :—

When an efficient strap with end pressure control is used it may be taken that failure occurs only when limiting values of strain have been reached both in compression and tension.

If then Y_+ represents this limiting strain value in tension and Y_- the limiting strain in compression, the length of the outer face of the bend will be given by $L(1+Y_+)$ and of the inner face by $L(1+Y_-)$, where L=initial length of specimen.

$$\therefore \frac{L(1+Y_+)}{L(1+Y_-)} = \frac{r+S}{r} \quad \text{where } r = \text{radius and } S = \text{thickness.}$$

$$\therefore \frac{S}{r} = \frac{Y_+ - Y_-}{1+Y_-} \quad \text{Note : } Y_- \text{ will have a negative value.}$$

Applying this formula to the limiting strain values given for beech on the curves we get

$$\frac{S}{r} = \frac{0.0105 + 0.29}{1 - 0.29} = \frac{0.3005}{0.71}$$

Thus if $S = 1$ inch, $r = \dfrac{0.71}{0.3005} = 2.3$ inches (approximately).

The limiting radius allowing for one rejected bend in twenty, as determined in practice on this species from actual bending tests, was 1.5 inches (see Table I).

The estimation of the minimum radius without support may be arrived at by putting $P = O$ in equation (5), since end pressure here is zero. Thus

$$O = BR \int_{e=\frac{r}{R}-1}^{e=Y_+} f(e)de$$

$$\text{i.e.} \int_{e=0}^{e=Y_+} f(e)\,de = \int_{e=0}^{e=\frac{r}{R}-1} f(e)\,de$$

Since $p = f(e)$ the value of $\displaystyle\int_{e=0}^{e=Y_+} f(e)\,de$ is given by the area under

the stress/stain curve for the wood in tension which, in the example given, may be taken as being roughly $\frac{1}{2}$ $(9500 \times 0.0105) = 52$ units. It thus follows that tension failure is about to occur when

$$\int_{e=0}^{e=\frac{r}{R}-1} f(e)\,de = 52, \text{ and it remains to find the value}$$

of the compressive strain such that the area under the compressive stress/strain relationship curve is also given as 52 units. In the example given it will be found that this corresponds roughly with a compressive strain of 5 per cent (-0.05).

Substituting in the equation $\dfrac{S}{r} = \dfrac{Y_+ + -Y_-}{1 + Y_-}$ we now get

$$\frac{S}{r} = \frac{0.0105 + 0.05}{1 - 0.05} = \frac{0.06}{0.95}$$

from which $r = 16$ inches when $S = 1$ inch.

The minimum radius as determined in practice on this species (unsupported) was 13 inches (see Table I).

Bending Moments

The bending moment M of the wood/strap system referred to the centre of the form and, measured by the torque in the table, is given by the equation:

$$M = B \int_{x=0}^{x=S} p_x(r+x)dx + P(r+S)$$

Rewriting this we get :

$$M = rB \int_{x=0}^{x=S} p_x dx + B \int_{x=0}^{x=S} x p_x dx + P(r+S)$$

Now $rB \int_{x=0}^{x=S} p_x dx = -Pr$, and $x = R(1+e_x) - r$ from (2)

$$\therefore \quad M = -Pr + B \int_{x=0}^{x=S} R(1+e_x) \, p_x dx - rB \int_{x=0}^{x=S} p_x dx + P(r+S)$$

$$= -Pr + RB \int_{x=0}^{x=S} p_x dx + BR \int_{x=\left(\frac{r}{R}-1\right)}^{x=\left(\frac{r+S}{R}-1\right)} Rf(e)e \, de + Pr + P(r+S)$$

$$= -RP + BR^2 \int_{e=\left(\frac{r}{R}-1\right)}^{e=\left(\frac{r+S}{R}-1\right)} f(e)e \, de \quad + P(r+S)$$

$$= P(r+S-R) + BR^2 \int_{e=\left(\frac{r}{R}-1\right)}^{e=\left(\frac{r+S}{R}-1\right)} f(e)e \, de \quad \dots\dots\dots\dots (6)$$

The equation for the bending moment given above consists of a couple, namely P multiplied by the distance between the neutral axis of the wood and the strap, plus a moment which varies as the square of the radius of the neutral axis of the wood.

The couple in the straight portion 0–0 to 2–2 is :

$$\frac{P\,S}{2}$$

This couple tends to cause the straight portion of the wood as it feeds on to the form to back-bend or " snake ", and it is to counteract this tendency that it is so necessary to provide bending straps with some form of back plate. In the above equations, M and P, the bending moments and end pressures, are given as functions of the unknown variable R, and it now remains to show the relation between R and β.

The strap length is assumed to remain unchanged ; therefore, the distance between end-stops measured along the strap remains unaltered during bending.

Hence the distance " d " between 0–0 and 2–2 is given by :

$$d = L - \beta\,(r+S)$$

The bent length of the wood between 0–0 and 1–1 is given by βR

$$\therefore \; \beta R + \frac{d}{1+e} = L$$

$$R = \frac{L\,(1+e)-d}{\beta(1+e)}$$

$$R = \frac{Le}{\beta(1+e)} + \frac{r+S}{1+e} \quad \cdots\cdots\cdots\cdots (7)$$

End pressure values $-P$ and bending moments M may now be found for any bending angle β from the stress/strain relationship curves, first by plotting the integral curve giving respectively the values of $\int pde$ and $\int pede$ with the values of strain " e " as abscissæ. Then by substituting arbitrary and numerous values of the radius of neutral axis R in equations (5) and (6), points on the curves giving the relationships between $-P$ and R, also M and R, may be found and graphs plotted. Finally, by substituting the values of R and e in equation (7), the relationship between $-P$, M and β can be established.

Comparison between Theoretical and Actual Bending Values

In order to compare the calculated end pressures and bending moments with those obtained in actual practice, a bending machine was designed and built capable of measuring both end pressures and bending moments during the actual bending operation. This machine is illustrated in Fig. 43 and consists of a revolving table " A " to which is fitted the bending form complete with metal strap and fixed end-stop " B ". To the other end of the strap is fitted a movable end-stop " C " which is adjustable by means of a hand wheel and worm drive " F ". In this adjustable end-stop system is incorporated a glycerine-filled cylinder " D " and pressure gauge " E " in such a manner that the pressure exerted by the end of the wood on the stop may be measured at any instant during bending.

This complete end-stop system, including a back-plate " G ", is free to slide along a guide arm " H " over a series of rollers. This guide arm is supported at either end on rollers, one set resting on the table and the other on a trestle. A radial pressure arm is arranged so as to press with a spring-loaded roller on the wood at the point of bending, and in this way to keep the bend pressed tightly to the face of the form.

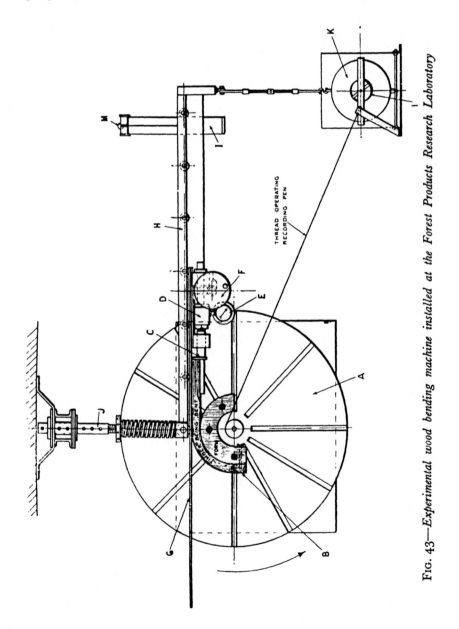

Fig. 43—*Experimental wood bending machine installed at the Forest Products Research Laboratory*

The guide arm is pivoted at one end to this radial pressure arm and, at the other, is fastened to a spring-loaded balance in such a manner that the back thrust or the resistance to bending of the piece can be measured. This balance pull is registered automatically on a chart and plotted against the angle through which the wood has been bent at any instant, so that by multiplying the reading by the length of the guide arm, the bending moment may be determined.

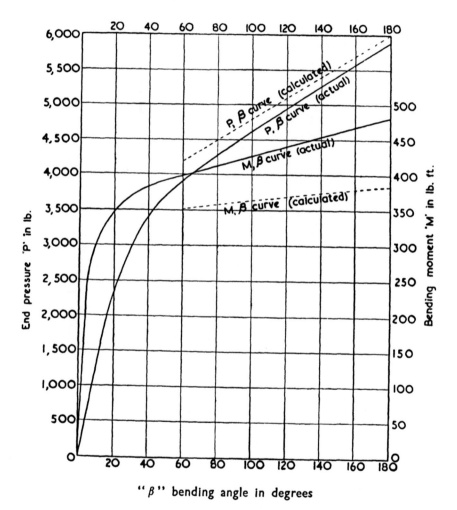

FIG. 44—*Curves showing the relationship between end pressures, bending moments and bending angle of home-grown beech*

Some typical curves showing the relationship between end pressures, bending moments and bending angle for English beech specimens 3 ft. long, 3 inches wide and $1\frac{1}{2}$ inches thick, bent to a radius of curvature of 8 inches, are given in Fig. 44. Calculated or theoretical curves determined from results of straightforward compression and tension tests on matched material are also shown in the figure in dotted form, from which some idea of the discrepancies between the two as obtained on the beech samples tested may be formed.

Comments

The method of determining the bending properties of steamed wood by standard type compression and tension tests, though economical in timber, could not be considered to yield results reliable or even reasonably accurate in practice.

The reasons for the discrepancies became apparent when it was observed in the actual bending operation that (*a*) initially plane sections did not remain plane, (*b*) friction between the wood and strap might become appreciable in amount, and (*c*) the radial pressures exerted by the strap often resulted in appreciable thinning of the section.

Still more serious difficulties arose in testing some of the exotic timbers of inferior bending qualities, when it was found virtually impossible to decide exactly at what stage during the compression of the test pieces failure occurred. Nevertheless, such tests often do provide some indication of the bending properties of timber and may yield data from which a better understanding of the principles of bending may be obtained.

It is, for example, interesting to note that the radius of the neutral axis in the wood varies with angle of bend and tends to increase with increase in this angle. In making heavy bends the neutral axis may well reach the convex face, in which case all the wood is in compression. It is in order to reduce somewhat the extent of this compression, and hence the liability to compression failure, that it often becomes advisable to reduce the end pressure by slackening off the adjustable end-stop and allowing as much stretch to take place as is possible without fracture. Again, it is possible to show theoretically how local stretching at the commencement of certain heavy bends, using straps with fixed end-stops, may be enough to cause fracture, in which case it will prove beneficial to adjust the end-stop initially so that pressure is applied to the wood before any of it is actually bent.

Movement of Bends

Loss or gain of moisture in a piece of bent wood will cause both its width and thickness to alter, but will not materially affect the longitudinal dimensions unless considerable compression has occurred in this direction. In laminated bends, longitudinal compressive strains are generally comparatively small and the laminæ behave, as far as dimensional changes due to moisture are concerned, in much the same way as in the unbent state. When, then, drying takes place in a bend that is " set " there is a tendency for the inner and outer surfaces to come closer together without any appreciable change occurring in the peripheral lengths of these surfaces. It is reasonable to suppose that in set laminated bends initially plane cross-sections of the piece tend to remain plane for relatively small moisture changes, in which case it becomes necessary for the radius of curvature of the bend to alter in order that the piece as a whole should conform to the dimensional changes that have occurred. Suppose the original thickness of a bend made to a form radius " r " to be " t " and that this shrinks by an amount " e " per unit of thickness, so that the final thickness of bend is $t(1-e)$. The peripheral lengths l_1 and l_2 of the inner and outer surfaces, respectively, remain virtually unchanged so that, if the assumption that plane sections remain plane is valid, then the following relation holds :

namely, $\dfrac{l_1}{r_1} = \dfrac{l_2}{r_1 + t(1-e)}$ where r_1 is the new radius of curvature,

but $l_1 = \dfrac{l_2 r}{r + t}$

So that $\dfrac{r}{r_1(r+t)} = \dfrac{1}{r_1 + t(1-e)}$

Hence $rr_1 + rt(1-e) = rr_1 + r_1 t$

or $r_1 = r(1-e)$.

This result is of interest as it indicates that the percentage decrease in radius of curvature should be exactly equal to the percentage decrease in the thickness of the bend caused by moisture loss, a result borne out by test.

Similarly, it can be shown that the unit increase in the angle of bend expressed in radians should be equal to $\dfrac{e}{1-e}$. Much the same reasoning may be applied to solid bends, except that here the movements are augmented by the fact that compressed wood tends to expand and shrink in the longitudinal direction with moisture gain and loss, and for this reason such bends are usually less stable than similar bends of laminated type. Finally, it follows that in both cases bends made from quartered material tend to " move " rather more than bends made from slash-cut material.

Supplement to Table I (p. 7)—Approximate Radius of Curvature (in Inches) at Which Breakages during Bending should not exceed 5 Per Cent.

Species	When supporting straps	
	are used	are not used
Abura (*Mitragyna ciliata*)	31.0	35.0
Acacia, False, *see* Robinia (p. 7)		
Afzelia (*Afzelia bipindensis*)	18.0	34.0
Afzelia (mbambakofi) (*Afzelia quanzensis*)	9.0	14.0
Agba (*Gossweilerodendron balsamiferum*)	20.0	16.0
Agboin, *see* Dahoma		
Albizzia (*Albizzia ferruginea*)	20.0	40.0
Alder (*Alnus glutinosa*)	14.0	18.0
Alstonia (*Alstonia congensis*)	31.0	—
Anopyxis (*Anopyxis ealænsis*)	40.0	60.0
Avodiré (*Turraeanthus africanus*)	36.0	38.0
Berlinia (*Berlinia* sp.)	17.5	19.5
Binuang (*Octomeles sumatrana*)	37.0	36.0
Coigue beech (*Nothofagus dombeyi*)	10.0	16.5
Cypress (*Podocarpus guatemalensis*)	35.0	36.0
Dahoma (*Piptadenia africana*)	15.0	29.0
Ebony, African (*Diospyros crassiflora*)	10.0	15.0
Ekhimi, *see* Dahoma		
Elm, European (*Ulmus procera*)	1.5	13.5
Elm, Rock (*Ulmus thomasi*)	1.5	14.0
Elm, White (*Ulmus americana*)	1.7	13.5
Elm, Wych (*Ulmus glabra*)	1.7	12.5
Essia (*Combretodendron africanum*)	36.0	27.0
Jarrah (*Eucalyptus marginata*)	17.5	39.0
Kokrodua (*Afrormosia elata*)	14.0	29.0
Krabak, *see* Mersawa		
Kurokai (*Protium decandrum*)	16.5	29.0
Laurel, Chilean (*Laurelia aromatica*)	17.0	19.5
Lime (*Tilia vulgaris*)	14.0	16.0
Mahogany, Sapele, *see* Sapele		
Makoré (*Mimusops heckelii*)	12.0	18.0
Mansonia (*Mansonia altissima*)	10.0	15.5
Mchenga (*Isoberlinia globiflora*)	15.0	32.0
Mersawa (*Anisoptera* spp.)	30.0	28.0
Mjombo (*Brachystegia boehmii*)	25.0	35.0
Mkwaju (*Tamarindus indica*)	12.5	33.0
Morabukea (*Mora gonggrijpii*)	11.5	32.0
Mubura (*Parinari excelsa*)	13.0	32.0
Muhimbi (*Cynometra alexandri*)	16.5	37.0
Muninga (*Pterocarpus angolensis*)	16.5	18.0
Mutondo (*Brachystegia ?spiciformis*)	32.0	40.0
Nyankom (*Tarrietia utilis*)	18.0	30.0
Ogea (*Daniellia ogea*)	50.0	28.0
Poplar, French (*Populus* sp.)	32.0	26.0
Pterygota (*Pterygota kamerunensis*)	36.0	33.0
Rauli (*Nothofagus procera*)	16.5	16.5
Ramin (*Gonystylus* sp.)	36.0	37.0
Sapele (*Entandrophragma cylindricum*)	30.0	37.0
Sterculia, Brown (*Sterculia rhinopetala*)	12.0	14.0
Sterculia, Yellow (*Sterculia oblonga*)	17.0	18.0
Sycamore (*Acer pseudoplatanus*)	1.5	14.5
" Teak, Rhodesian " (*Baikiaea plurijuga*)	13.0	25.0
Utile (*Entandrophragma utile*)	36.0	40.0

Species	Thickness of laminæ (Inches)	Average moisture content (Per cent)	Radius in ins. at which losses due to break-ages did not ex-ceed 5 per cent of the pieces bent	Approximate ratio: radius/ thickness of laminæ
Abura (*Mitragyna ciliata*)	0.125	12.8	6.0	48
Afzelia (*Afzelia bipindensis*)	0.125	10.9	9.5	76
Agba (*Gossweilerodendron balsamiferum*)	0.125	12.4	4.4	35
Albizzia (*Albizzia ferruginea*)	0.125	12.0	7.0	56
Alder (*Alnus glutinosa*)	0.125	12.2	7.4	59
Ash (home-grown) (*Fraxinus excelsior*)	0.125	13.5	4.8	38
Avodiré (*Turraeanthus africanus*)	0.125	13.1	7.2	57
Ayan (*Distemonanthus benthamianus*)	0.125	10.4	7.3	58
Baromalli (*Catostemma commune*)	0.125	11.5	6.3	50
Berlinia (*Berlinia* sp.)	0.125	12.2	5.4	43
Binuang (*Octomeles sumatrana*)	0.125	14.2	7.3	58
Camphorwood, Borneo (*Dryobalanops* sp.)	0.125	13.0	7.3	58
Coigue (*Nothofagus dombeyi*)	0.125	11.3	6.4	51
Dahoma (*Piptadenia africana*)	0.125	11.0	8.5	68
Daniellia (*Daniellia ogea*)	0.125	11.5	8.4	67
Danta (*Cistanthera papaverifera*)	0.125	14.2	5.3	42
Ebony, African (*Diospyros crassiflora*)	0.125	11.8	5.1	41
Ekhimi, *see* Dahoma				
Elm, European (*Ulmus procera*)	0.125	12.3	5.8	46
Elm, Rock (*Ulmus thomasi*)	0.125	13.1	3.8	31
Elm, White (*Ulmus americana*)	0.125	13.6	4.3	34
Elm, Wych (*Ulmus glabra*)	0.125	11.5	4.6	37
Essia (*Combretodendron africanum*)	0.125	11.9	6.4	51
Freijo (*Cordia goeldiana*)	0.125	12.0	7.3	58
Greenheart (*Ocotea rodiaei*)	0.125	12.9	6.3	50
Guarea, Scented (*Guarea cedrata*)	0.125	13.2	7.9	63
Hornbeam (*Carpinus betulus*)	0.125	12.8	6.3	50
Horse-chestnut (*Aesculus hippocastanum*)	0.125	12.3	5.3	42
Idigbo (*Terminalia ivorensis*)	0.125	12.8	7.5	60
Jarrah (*Eucalyptus marginata*)	0.125	12.7	6.8	54
Kokrodua (*Afrormosia elata*)	0.125	10.6	6.5	52
Krabak (*Anisoptera* spp.)	0.125	12.5	7.0	56

[continued overleaf

Species	Thickness of laminæ (Inches)	Average moisture content (Per cent)	Radius in ins. at which losses due to breakages did not exceed 5 per cent of the pieces bent	Approximate ratio: radius/ thickness of laminæ
Laurel, Chilean (*Laurelia aromatica*)	0.125	12.3	6.8	54
Lime (*Tilia vulgaris*)	0.125	10.8	7.0	56
Maho (*Sterculia pruriens*)	0.125	12.8	6.5	52
Mahogany, African (*Khaya ivorensis*)	0.125	13.7	6.0	48
Makoré (*Mimusops heckelii*)	0.125	13.0	6.2	49
Mansonia (*Mansonia altissima*)	0.125	13.5	4.3	34
Mbambakofi (*Afzelia quanzensis*)	0.125	13.7	7.1	57
Mchenga (*Isoberlinia globiflora*)	0.125	12.9	6.8	54
Mersawa, *see* Krabak				
Mjombo (*Brachystegia boehmii*)	0.125	12.4	6.8	54
Mkwaju (*Tamarindus indica*)	0.125	14.5	6.9	55
Mora (*Mora excelsa*)	0.125	12.9	6.1	49
Morabukea (*Mora gonggrijpii*)	0.125	11.8	9.5	76
Mubura (*Parinari excelsa*)	0.125	13.9	6.5	52
Muhimbi (*Cynometra alexandri*)	0.125	14.4	7.3	58
Muninga (*Pterocarpus angolensis*)	0.125	10.7	6.8	55
Mutondo (*Brachystegia ?spiciformis*)	0.125	11.6	7.3	58
Nyankom (*Tarrietia utilis*)	0.125	12.6	7.4	59
Oak, American white (*Quercus* spp.)	0.125	13.3	5.4	43
Ogea, *see* Daniellia				
Olive, E. African (*Olea hochstetteri*)	0.125	10.6	8.0	64
Opepe (*Sarcocephalus diderrichii*)	0.125	12.4	9.7	78
Poplar (French) (*Populus* sp.)	0.125	12.3	6.3	50
Pterygota (*Pterygota kamerunensis*)	0.125	11.1	6.2	49
" Queensland walnut " (*Endiandra palmerstonii*)	0.125	12.1	7.4	59
Ramin (*Gonystylus* sp.)	0.125	12.4	9.0	72
Rauli (*Nothofagus procera*)	0.125	12.1	7.5	60
Sapele (*Entandrophragma cylindricum*)	0.125	13.8	6.3	50
Sterculia, Brown (*Sterculia rhinopetala*)	0.125	13.6	4.5	36
Sterculia, Yellow (*Sterculia oblonga*)	0.125	12.8	6.4	51
Sycamore (*Acer pseudoplatanus*)	0.125	13.3	4.1	32
" Teak, Rhodesian " (*Baikiaea plurijuga*)	0.125	10.6	6.5	52
Utile (*Entandrophragma utile*)	0.125	11.4	8.3	66
Wamara (*Swartzia leiocalycina*)	0.125	13.5	7.5	60
Yew (*Taxus baccata*)	0.125	12.1	6.8	54

INDEX

LaVergne, TN USA
28 September 2009
159246LV00011B/186/A